D1591543

CROW IN THE HOUSE, WOLF AT THE DOOR

A Memoir

CROW IN THE HOUSE, WOLf AT THE DOOR

A Memoir

fRANCES NAIL

CITY DESK PRESS
AUSTIN, TEXAS

Cover Illustration: Portrait of Catherine Key Ayers Clark by Katy Nail
Editor: Leslie Nail

ACKNOWLEDGEMENTS

My thanks to Ken Hammond, editor of "Texas," the Sunday magazine of the *Houston Chronicle,* for publishing many of these essays, and because, in lieu of rejection slips, he sent me writing lessons.

And my thanks to John Aielli for loving these stories and for letting me read them on his famous program, "Eklektikos," of PBS radio affiliate KUT, The University of Texas, Austin.

This book
was written with love
for my mother and father,

CATHERINE KEY AYERS CLARK
1887-1977

FREDERICK VIVIEN CLARK
1881-1971

CONTENTS

Just south the long plains
crumble down cliffs
to a rolling which was once the ocean bed.
Behind you the squat town dwindles.
Across the street the crops begin,
a stretch of cotton and sunflowers.
Grandmother your house sits on the edge.

My uncles squint over their fields,
tilted heads wondering
who ever convinced them
to plant a season of sunflowers.
There was money in the seeds.
Now there are sunflowers in the cotton.
Grandmother you laugh.
They nod at you from the fields.

Someone put down this house
on a square bit of ground
where cotton grew,
now just lawn and a young pecan tree.

In town there was a house
that grew grandchildren and zinnias,
sweet pecans cracked by the rocker.
A crow lived there, your pet.
He rode your head to burn the trash.
He pecked my mother's toes.

At sunset the late spring clouds come up.
The flat plains can't stop them.
Hail and lightning, squirming funnels
sweep over the crops.
Somewhere cotton and sunflowers fly up.
The neighbors pour into their cellars.
You stand in the window, tempting tornadoes.

GRANDMOTHER YOUR HOUSE
Leslie Nail

WHEN PEARS AND LILACS BLOOMED

I don't know how she spelled her name, but we called her Lee Etta.

I think that she was pretty. I know that her skin was the color of good hot chocolate and that she had big, sweet eyes. She was slim, skinny maybe, and I can still see her long brown fingers turning, smoothing and ironing my daddy's starched white shirts. He was a druggist and wore six to work and one on Sunday. She lived in an old shack in our back yard under two tremendous pear trees. It had a little room on one end that had stored our coal when we used potbellied stoves. When Lee Etta came, we had gas, and she used the coal room for bathing in a washtub and for her slop jar on winter nights. Otherwise, she used a privy out near the alley. We had electricity, but she still had a kerosene lamp.

Our house, which we always called "the big old white house" after we lost it in the Depression, was not big at all. It had two front bedrooms, a sleeping porch at the back, and a little room, really just a big closet, with a bed and racks for clothes. We did have a grand front porch, screened by two huge lilacs.

Lee Etta was not our maid; we were too poor for maids. She paid her rent helping with the washing and ironing. Actually, she stood by for the washing. My mother moved too fast and had no patience with help when she was washing. She boiled our white stuff in a big black pot and scrubbed, rinsed, and wrung it out in tubs under the pear trees. Fortunately for Lee Etta, we hung up our school clothes and played in coveralls, which we wore until they were stiff. But she ironed most of it. I loved her, followed her around and thought that she was a woman. I was about six. When I look back, I know that she was no more than sixteen, if that.

The day C.D. came, I was in the top of the pear trees. The trees were snow-white with bloom. The lilacs were blooming, as well, and my mother's sweet peas and larkspur and petunias around our dirt yard. The whole place had a heavenly smell.

C.D. . . . I wish there were a way to more than capitalize his name. He was the most elegant man. I thought that surely he was a movie star. He came on the train but arrived at our house on a wagon with a mule driven by an old black man. He came with a trunk and a suitcase. A trunk! I had never seen one out of an attic. He was tall, with great sad eyes and a mustache. He was the color of khaki and wore a white shirt and tie. He carried a coat. I froze to the tree as he knocked on Lee Etta's door. She came out, paused, and in a timeless cool way said, "Oh. Hello." And then she fell all apart, weeping and hugging and laughing and kissing C.D. Slowly, with the help of the old man, they took his trunk and his suitcase into her house and closed the door. When I could move, I scrambled down and flew to the house to announce that *somebody* had come to Lee Etta's!

We had never seen clothes like C.D.'s on anyone, black or white. Blazers, creamy slacks, and gray pinstriped pants, beautiful shirts and a white suit. He was handsome. He moved right in as if to stay with Lee Etta, and our eyes followed them everywhere, and the pears and the lilacs were blooming. They walked out in the evenings arm in arm, Lee Etta in her best and C.D. in his Clark Gable clothes. But most of the time, except when Lee Etta was cleaning her houses, they stayed in her room or sat under the pear trees.

One night in the fall, Lee Etta and C.D. went down to the flats. Down past the railroad tracks, past the cottonseed mill and the compress to the flats (its real name was Morning Side) where most black people lived and where they went to church, school, and to dance. Lee Etta and C.D. went to dance. At midnight, Lee Etta pounded on our back door, calling, "Miz Clock! Miz Clock!" Her arms were loaded, and she said C.D. was after her clothes and to please take them. My mother hung them in the little room, and Lee Etta went back to her shack and waited.

Near dawn, Lee Etta was beating on the door again. "Miz Clock! C.D. is beatin' the hell outa me!" My mother pulled her in and told her to go to bed. Mother, daddy, brother, sister and I were sleeping on the sleeping porch, my oldest sister and her new husband in the little room. A full house, but Lee Etta went to bed. I can't remember where, but I have always hoped it was with me. Our front rooms were occupied by boarders, two engineers and their wives, who had come to survey the Red River for President Roosevelt, feeding us at the same time with their board money.

My mother went out to confront C.D. "C.D., get your clothes and get from here! This is Lee Etta's home and nobody, *nobody*, mistreats her here. Don't let me catch you here tomorrow!"

C.D. went the next morning with his trunk full of shreds. Down in the flats, C.D. had taken up with a pretty woman and had danced the night away with her. Lee Etta came home, took her scissors and cut up his beautiful clothes. She cut the arms off his jackets and shirts. She cut the legs off his trousers, and she snipped the white suit to bits. We were sad about the white suit. I am still sad about it, the first white suit I had ever known.

Next day, my mother asked Lee Etta why she didn't call for Mr. Clark when C.D. was beating her. She said, "Miz Clock, you know nobody is afred of Mr. Clock." But that is another story.

Lee Etta crept back to her shack in the morning. She didn't come out or answer her door for days, though we all hovered around calling to her. She was never the same. Before C.D., she had walked as if she were dancing, laughing a lot and telling funny stories. Now she shuffled around in a ragged black dress and would not smile. The pear trees were losing their leaves and it was cold. When my mother said Lee Etta had lost her bloom, I cried. I tried to make her smile. "Lee Etta, Ma made oatmeal cookies. Lee Etta, Ma made chocolate pies. Lee Etta, I've brought a game. Lee Etta, I've got a hornit toad." Her favorite things, but she would only respond, "Lea' me 'lone, chile," or "Go 'way, chile."

She mourned and grieved around all winter, dragging the iron over the white shirts and trudging off to her work. Before the lilacs and pears bloomed again, she was gone.

This all happened down on Seventh Street in Memphis, Texas, out in the Red River Valley on the Prairie Dog Fork of the Red at the foot of the Palo Duro Canyon. Sixty-three years later, I never see a white bloom or smell anything lavender or lilac that I don't think of C.D. and Lee Etta. Where did they go? What did they do? C.D. with no clothes. Lee Etta with no love.

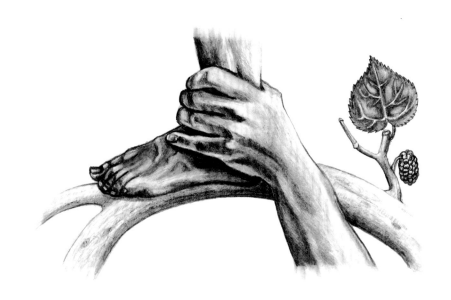

THE WHISKEY INCIDENT AND OTHER MEMORABLE EVENTS

For us, 1929 was a very good year. The stock market crashed, but we were already poor and had nothing to lose. Or so we thought. I was five years old and my sister Loisie was a flapper. At least I thought she was, but she was a fake flapper. She didn't drink or smoke and she didn't even know how to be "fast," but she cut off her hair, freaking us out. She and her girl friends wore little cloche hats and short flippy skirts. They put the latest celluloid records on our old Victrola and did the Charleston, a scandalous dance in our town. They played "Ramona" over and over until I knew it by heart. "Ramona, when evening falls, I'll hear your call. Ramona, we'll meet beside the waterfall." And I thought that "Toot-Toot-Tootsie, Goodbye" was my song, because my name at the time was "Toot."

Loisie fell in love with her husband-to-be and I was thrilled. It wasn't just the romance; it was his car. We had no car and here was this knight coming to our rescue in a two-toned roadster with orange wire wheels and a rumble seat. He was new in town, unusual when so few came. He was also handsome and he had a great name, George Washington Carter. I loved it, and to think that my sister had caught him was almost more than I could stand. He and Loisie would roar around town in that roadster with my brother and me in the rumble seat, waving and laughing uncontrollably with the pure bliss of it.

And so, in 1929, we were happy. Even though we had lost a brother the year before. We had survived and were smiling again and even laughing a little. We were getting a new brother and didn't know yet about the Depression to come. We didn't know yet what poor was. We didn't know that our old white house (which those of us alive still love) and our father's drugstore would be gone with the winds that brought the terrible dustbowl days, covering our poverty with dirt. We were like people on a picnic at the edge of an abyss who had spread their quilt too close to the edge. Ignorance really is bliss, and we had plenty of both.

My best friend that year was a little boy named J.K. I have had only two spankings in my life, and I was playing with J.K. both times. I was also playing with him when I put the rock in my ear and the day we found the whiskey. I was forbidden to play with some children who lived down the street and to eat mulberries from their tree. My mother would never tell me why, only that they were "common." They did say "I seen," but I played with some who said much worse. The mulberries, she said, would give me worms. J.K. and I were up in the mulberry tree with purple mouths when her hand clamped around my ankle. I was yanked out of the tree, dragged home and spanked with a cake turner. I can still feel the shock of it. A first spanking at five is memorable. My siblings sneered about the unfairness of it, saying that they had had plenty of whippings. My mother used to say that by the time I was born, she was too tired to care and had found that spanking made not one whit of difference.

My other spanking was simply the result of bad timing. Every Saturday morning we bathed, dressed up, and went to town. If we had a dime, we went to the movies. Otherwise, we walked around the square and hung out in my father's drugstore until closing. He didn't close his doors until the last soul had left the square, so we walked home very late. Once in a while, Bob Wills and his Texas Playboys would come from Turkey, put up a bandstand and play a concert on the courthouse lawn. This stirred everybody up and a big, happy crowd would mill around the square until all hours.

On a Bob Wills morning, while waiting for my turn in the tub, I wandered off with J.K. to the cotton gins. I wasn't supposed to be there alone and J.K. didn't count as a person. We were running over the cotton bales when I heard my mother calling. "FRANK! Fraaank!" I hated her calling me Frank. For one thing, I was a girl, and for another, she only called me Frank when she "meant business." I hit the ground running and met her half way home. She was carrying a big switch that looked like the limb of a tree to me. She switched my legs every time she caught up with me all the way home. I was clean but still squalling when we got to town.

The rock in my ear wouldn't have been memorable (children have always put things in their ears and lots of other places), but occurring as it did the week after the gin incident, it was memorable because I decided not to mention it. I knew that my mother would have to leave her work and walk with me the twelve blocks to the doctor, and I knew that she couldn't pay him. J.K. and I were playing on a pile of gravel, picking out the little pebbles, when I pushed one into my ear. I was deaf and miserable for days. The small white stone grew to feel like a big black boulder. Finally, as nonchalantly as I could manage, I said, "Ma, I do believe that something is the matter with my ear." Indeed. It was Frank, Frank, Frank all the way to the doctor.

Memphis, for a little town, had plenty of bootleggers. There was even a gun battle that year between our permanent bootlegger and one of the fly-by-nighters. Fortunately, they were terrible shots, but the sound of it was so unheard in our little town that people for blocks around spent the rest of the night nervously peering out windows and the whole town shuddered and shook for days. The day that J.K. and I found the whiskey, we were playing in the alley behind Miss Ezzell's house.

There was a great mound of new-mown grass against the fence. It was so soft and smelled so sweet that we jumped and flopped in it until it was no longer a pile but was dispersed all over the alley. At the bottom, we found about twelve half-gallon jars, full of an amber liquid. We decided to ask Miss Ezzell what it might be, so we took one of the jars and knocked on her back door. Miss Ezzell took one whiff and gasped, "Oh, my goodness! That's whiskey!" She poured it on the ground.

J.K. and I retreated to the alley to think. "Let's not give Miss Ezzell any more of our whiskey," I said. "Let's take one to my Ma." We did. She was standing by the kitchen sink, but she didn't pour the whiskey down it. She put her finger in it and tasted. "Oh, man! *That* is whiskey!" she said. "Is there any more?" She was pleased to pass out the rest of it to her favored friends. She was so happy about that whiskey that I felt vindicated for all the trouble that I had caused her by eating the mulberries and running off to the gins and putting the rock in my ear.

RUNNING WILD

I was a member of a gang when I was five years old. My brother John, seven, and I were the youngest members. Not the youngest children on Seventh Street, but the youngest allowed to run wild. As in "She just lets those kids run *wild.*" Our gang didn't have guns, unless you count rubber guns. A rubber gun is a stock cut out of a board with thin circles cut from an inner tube and stretched over it, held and released by clothespins. It could raise a big welt on your arm, but it wouldn't, like gang weapons today, blow your arm plumb off.

Our gang was like the gang in "Our Gang Comedy," but older, wiser, and wilder. My sister Bob, who called herself Roberta Victoria though her name is Bobby Ayers, was the boss of us all, but Billy Ed was the star. Billy Ed was not William Edward; his name was Billy Ed. He had a horse and a donkey. There were cows, goats, and chickens on Seventh

Street, but only one horse and one donkey. Billy Ed rode that horse through the neighborhood like a ten-year-old god. He ran over me once, when he was chasing the gang. They were running for Miss Ezzell's fence, and I was sitting on her path, digging a hole. The horse only bruised and scraped my heel, but it gave me my fear of looking up at horses.

Miss Ezzell's fence reminds me that we smoked. She had a wire fence with cedar posts. We would build a little fire behind her garage, strip pieces of bark from the posts, and roll them in newspaper. A lieutenant would then climb to the top of a locust tree, where Bob, the captain, had her lookout post, to ask for permission to smoke. After two or three puffs, Bob would shout, "No Smoking!" We put them out. We were followers then as gang members are today. It was a blessing in this case, as the hot smoke from a cedar post cigarette is a killer.

A little curb bordered our front yard. We sat there on summer nights, eavesdropping and waiting. The neighbors, laughing and telling stories on our front porch, flicked their cigarettes over the lilacs. We finished them.

Billy Ed had carnivals. Chicken carnivals. He dressed his pet chickens in doll and old baby clothes and put them in a little tent. Admission was a penny. I hated those miserable chickens. They intimidated me with their glaring eyes, but I dutifully gave him my penny and sat in with them awhile; otherwise, I might not have had a ride on his donkey.

Billy Ed loved those silly chickens. His mother once bought one from him for a quarter. He ate that fried chicken, sobbing and crying with every bite. One of his chickens got into Mrs. Offield's garden. She wrung its neck and threw it over the fence. Billy Ed bided his time and, in a few days, let a couple of *her* chickens into her garden. She wrung their necks and threw them over the fence. His mother cooked them for supper.

One day, Mrs. Offield was working over a flower bed when we all sauntered by. Billy Ed gave her a whack across her seat, causing her to fall into the bed. We scattered. Billy's sister Ruthie ran home and got under the living room couch. Mrs. Offield took a kitchen knife and went to their house and said, "I have come to wait for the person who pushed me into my flower bed." She sat on the couch, under which poor Ruthie was sweating and trying not to breathe. Mrs. Offield sat there smiling for an hour. Billy Ed never gave himself up.

We had cookouts. Late in the afternoon, we went home for food and equipment. We came back with a skillet, some pie pans for plates, and, if lucky, bacon, eggs, and potatoes. We always built the fire in Zeb Junior's ditch. No adults came to say, "Don't burn yourselves, don't do this, don't do that." We did it ourselves and sat around the fire in the dark, talking of how good the food was and of ghosts and stars and death. The stars in the Memphis sky sixty-five years ago were so awesome that a gang member today might change his ways, could he see them. We speculated on our chances of living to be a hundred. The potatoes were never quite right.

We stuffed our pockets with anything edible and went to the creek. The creek, running down from the Palo Duro Canyon to Memphis past the bottom of Seventh Street, was a clear, clean stream in a broad, flat, sandy bed. Five or six inches deep most of the time, it was lined on the cliff side with great gypsum boulders. We ran and jumped endlessly over those rocks until, near heat stroke, we fell into the water to cool off and have a drink. Before we drank, if we thought to do it, we would send someone upstream to look for a dead cow in the water. We never found one, and paid no attention to the manure that was sometimes bobbing about. We would then walk in the water down to Boy Scout Canyon, which had been carved out by the creek in a time that was beyond our knowing.

There, we climbed straight up to a little ledge and inched our way to Boy Scout Cave. Or at least, everyone else did. I never saw the cave. The first time that I climbed to the ledge, I froze. Had to be lowered down, kid by kid. I got my fear of heights there.

I preferred dirt yard caves. We had plenty of dirt yards. A yard cave is a major undertaking. Many have to dig with shovels and spades, until there is a hole about six feet square and deep enough to sit in. A tunnel is dug at least three feet long, but only deep enough to slither through. Boards must be found to cover it and the dirt piled back on top. Finally, someone has to get a flashlight or a candle. No grownup eye can see into a yard cave.

Billy Ed (in secret and all alone) dug a cave that must have been six feet deep. He then invited us all in, where we fell like lemmings into the dark, a shrieking, moaning pile. Maybe it wasn't as deep as I remember. None of us were hurt.

I looked up to Martha Jane, Billy Ed's twin sister, because of her overalls. She wore blue-striped overalls with suspenders and they made a lovely swishing sound when she walked. I had to wear tacky little gray handed-down coveralls. They had been washed so many times, they made no sound at all. Once, when I was near death from pneumonia, my Aunt Gus asked if there was anything she could get for me. My voice was so weak that she had to put her ear near my mouth, but I whispered, "Blue-striped overalls."

I found a dollar bill one day. A dollar was at that time a lot of money. I was wearing my overalls and Martha Jane happened along in hers. I said, "Look what I have found!" "Come with me," she said. We swished our way to the little store where there was a glass-fronted case crammed with penny candy. For the dollar, we each had a sack with fifty big pieces of candy, jaw-breakers, bubble gum, Tootsie Rolls, chocolates, taffy, licorice sticks, and other marvelous things that my memory has lost. My taste buds still remember. My mother had a conniption fit when she saw that candy and heard about the dollar. A dime, at that time, would buy a gallon of fresh milk from Mammy Franks, with the cream still rising.

A mile or two east of Seventh Street, by the railroad tracks, were the cotton gins with cotton bales leaning like dominoes in long, long rows. We leaped from bale to bale and jumped in a giant pile of cottonseed. We were forbidden to jump in the cottonseed, where some hobos had suffocated one cold winter night. But we jumped there anyhow. I sometimes wonder that we all survived, none injured or lost.

We took off our shoes when school was out, except for Sunday School. Our soles became impervious to the rocks on the gravel streets and the heat of the red brick roads. If we stepped on a nail or were hit with something and came in bleeding, my mother would search for the object to see if it was rusty. If it was, we were taken for a tetanus shot. I often bled, but I never qualified for a shot. We thought that tetanus (we knew it as "lockjaw") was caused by rust. Oh, we were ignorant.

We were ignorant, but we were as free as the breezes that blew off the prairies. No doors were locked; we went in and out at will, eating our way from kitchen to kitchen. Zeb Junior could sound exactly like an injured dog, which he often did, howling out our kitchen window while my mother beat him with a cup towel. John and Benjy were howling in the back yard one day, having stood in a red ant bed until their clothes were full of ants. My mother stripped off their clothes and squirted them down with the hose. They were horrified to be "nekkid" in the back yard, with the gang snickering around.

Another time, they went under the house, where the dogs slept. They came out covered with dirt and fleas, crawled in a window and lay down on a clean, white bed. Ma dragged them back to the yard and stripped them of their clothes again, only this time she tried to drown them instead of the fleas.

Unlike gang members of today, we never intentionally hurt anyone. Except in the boxing ring. Billy Ed and Zeb Junior put one up in Zeb's back yard. They had boxing gloves and fights with much shouting and crying. One day, they put the gloves on Cullen and me. We were the same age, though he was taller. But Cullen had not been educated in the ways of a gang. I won and he was chased crying back to Mrs. Offield, who was baby-sitting him that summer. Cullen was smarter than any of us. He had a wonderful, sly sense of humor. I had a secret crush on him until after we graduated, years later in Lubbock. In my long, long list of regrets, I regret the most that I made Cullen cry.

Oh, we were noisy, running and shouting, squalling and fighting, throwing balls over houses all day long. Red Rover, Red Rover, come over, come over. Playing hide-and-seek at night, delicious in the dark. Annie, Annie Oakley, one two three, everybody out, come in free.

I love my old gang. The Crump kids, whose widowed mother cooked hash-browned potatoes every night, causing us to hang around their kitchen window. Billy Ed, Martha Jane, their big sister Ruthie, their cousin Jim Bob. Benjy. Athalee, whom we called "Nink Fat" and who jumped, on a dare from Billy Ed, from his roof to the garage, breaking her leg. Zeb Junior, a beautiful, only child, crazy and funny and the girls all loved him. I still do. Roberta Victoria. I love to say their names.

We are old now and many of us dead. Jim Bob died young. Martha Jane died last year. Ruthie killed herself long ago.

She parked her car on a little country road by the golf course. Martha Jane, who was playing golf, heard the shot. Benjy and Zeb Junior are gone. I heard that Billy Ed has Alzheimer's. Bobby Ayers, my sister and our captain, has lost her memory.

When we were a gang, we were like Dylan Thomas in his poem "Fern Hill." "In the sun born over and over, we ran our heedless ways." Little we cared that time would take us, or that we would wake one morning to find the caves and the creeks and the cotton bales "forever fled from the childless land."

In my old age, I have a front porch looking out on Lake Travis. The voices are back on my porch, off and on, but I don't hear children's voices. I know that they are here; I see them getting off the school buses. But I don't hear "Red Rover, Red Rover." Nobody throws a ball over my house or digs a cave or builds a fire in my back yard. I don't hear mothers calling at bedtime. I don't hear, "Everybody out, come in free."

Nobody comes in free today. Children aren't allowed to play far from home, for fear they will not return. The summer night voices, the laughing, murmuring voices, have ceased. Everyone has gone inside and closed the windows. The porches are abandoned. The doors are closed and locked. The fun is done.

MAD DOGS AND CATS

I must have been about four when my first cat went mad.
I can't remember its name, but I remember the pain when
my sister Loisie grabbed me by my hair and arm and yanked
me up on an old dresser on our sleeping porch. She had
jumped up there when the cat went absolutely bananas, yowling and clawing and spitting and racing over the beds, a furry
ball of insanity. My mother, hearing the crying and yowling,
knew exactly what was happening. She raced in with her
broom and swept the cat out the back door, where it made
one last grand leap high into the air and fell to the ground,
as dead as a doornail.

We must have known about the rabies vaccine in Memphis
out in the Red River Valley in the twenties and thirties.

But, if we did, there was no money for it. Pasteur found the rabies virus in 1881 and made an immunization for animals, ten daily injections. He saved a boy who had been severely bitten by a rabid dog in 1885 with a similar immunization. No dog or cat that I ever knew was vaccinated. Leashes were unheard of, much less leash laws, and unless a dog was vicious it was not confined.

The day the cat went mad in 1928, it never occurred to my mother to get shots for me. I'm sure I had been playing with that cat all morning. She thought you had to have a bite. I am pleased to be alive.

But my mother constantly warned us about dogs. "If you meet a strange dog, and it is staggering around and frothing at the mouth, run like the wind away from it." This gave me a terrible fear of strange dogs. I can't run like the wind anymore, but if I meet a strange dog, frothing or not, my hackles rise, and I break out in a frightened sweat.

The day I found that I had a brain and was glad to be a girl, I was on my way up the alley to the little store where we went to buy penny candy. There was an old chow dog on that alley who hated boys. He had never bothered me. But on that day, I was wearing my first pair of jeans. The chow rushed out, snarling, his hair standing up on his neck. I froze. I thought. And then I decided not to panic. I looked him in the eye and rolled my jeans up to my knees. The chow smiled and went back into his yard. I went on to the store with my penny, thinking, "What a smart girl I am!"

Memories are peculiar things. One advantage of writing old family tales at my age is that most of the old family is gone, no one left to question your memories. I have only my sister, Bob, who has lost hers, and my brother, John, who quibbles with me. His memory isn't worth a durn. He thinks it was on the front porch of the little brown house where we were born that our dog went mad and bit our cousin Chuck. But in that case, I wouldn't remember it. And I do remember it. It couldn't have happened at the brown house, for we moved from that house to Quanah when I was six months old. John would have been only two and a half, before he lost what is known as our three-year amnesia. We moved back to Memphis and boarded awhile with Mammy Powell and then got our big old white house before I was three. We almost grew up there, before we lost it in the Depression. When the dog bit Chuck, he was on the porch of the *white* house.

The way I remember it, we were playing with our cousins, Chuck, Mary, and Hubert, a toddler, on the porch. Ruth wasn't born yet. We had all been playing with the dog when it threw a snapping, snarling fit and bit Chuck. We ran screaming into the front bedroom. My daddy, or uncle, came with my daddy's double-barreled shotgun and shot the dog from the window. A traumatic event. His head was sent off. He had rabies and Chuck had to have the awful shots over a period of weeks. No thought was given to the rest of us. What lucky children we were, not to have died of rabies.

Could the deafening blast from my daddy's old gun, the screaming children, and the dead dog have been programmed into my brain from stories until it was mine? I don't think so, but I wish I could remember the dog's name. I think it was our little Boston bull, who ate a celluloid doll and got as sick as a horse. I do remember my mother working on the dog in the bathroom, giving him enemas and other remedies, which I don't like to recall, until he survived. I never heard the word "veterinarian" until I was grown.

After that dog, we got a beautiful German shepherd that we called Prince. Prince grew huge and my mother thought he was dangerous. She gave him to friends on a farm. We visited him there, but John and I grieved for him. One day we met a great, white, shaggy dog on our way home from school. We coaxed him home, fed him and called him Old Prince. He followed us, we said, and Ma let us keep him. I think he was a cross between collie and St. Bernard. He reached to our shoulders. He had a big, square head and a sweet, intelligent face. I would take a book outside to read. Old Prince, seeing the book, would race to our spot under a locust tree and flop down, becoming a great, soft pillow. I would lean back and read aloud to him, stroking his ears. He loved the stories.

The night Old Prince went mad we were all sleeping on the front porch. On summer nights, during heat waves, we dragged our mattresses to the porch and one to an old iron bedstead in the back yard. We fought over that back yard bed, as the stars, before city lights, were worth the price of the mosquitoes. It was the same all over town; you were as safe asleep in your yard as in the house, for no doors were locked.

On one of those hot summer nights, Old Prince was sleeping under the lilac bushes that shielded our porch from the street. Near dawn, he began thrashing around, barking and breaking the lilacs. He growled and snapped at the branches and took off up Seventh Street, howling. We all sat up, wide-eyed. My mother said, "Old Prince has gone mad." None of us slept the rest of that night. My mother said in the morning that Old Prince ran because "even mad dogs don't want to harm their own."

We learned the next day that Old Prince had run all the way past Main Street. He ran into the Hudgins' back yard, snarling, snapping, and lunging. Mr. Hudgins, knowing immediately what he was faced with, jumped up and grabbed a hoe, which was leaning against a tree. He held Old Prince off with the hoe, while his wife ran in to get the gun. She shot poor Old Prince in his side.

The Hudgins called the next morning to tell us of their bad night with Old Prince, and how sorry they were to have killed him. That was the way things were in those days; you were even sorry to have killed a mad dog.

We took an old sheet and went after him, bringing him home in our red wagon. We buried him in the vacant lot, our pet cemetery. We had a funeral, with eulogies, as always. His stone was an old piece of cement, on which we wrote, "Old Prince, our dog." Old Prince lies there still, among our many other pets. The little dog (minus his head) who bit Chuck; Josie, a darling white dog who was poisoned by Old Man Franks because she nipped at his heels every time he passed our house; Grayling, my favorite cat, who would lie on his back in my doll's bed when I pretended he was sick, putting a wet handkerchief on his forehead; Black Mammy, a beautiful black Persian that we called Black Man until she began to have dozens of cats. My Christmas present, she was the only cat we ever bought. My daddy loved that cat and Black Man slept under the cover at the foot of his bed. Dad woke up one morning with a batch of kittens wrapped around his feet. Black Man became Black Mammy that day.

And then there was my orange cat—I think I called him Fluffy. I had gone to Clarendon to visit Loisie and her new husband. A neighbor of theirs gave me Fluffy. He was nearly grown. I was sent back to Memphis with two old men in an old touring car, or maybe a Ford Model A. All I remember is the back seat. The old men drove along at thirty miles per hour, the thirty miles to Memphis, talking of their bad crops and the Depression. They never once looked back to see me fighting the big cat in the back seat. The car was open, no windows. The cat kept lunging to get out and it became a battle of wills, whether Fluffy would disappear into the coun-tryside or I would take him home. They finally put me out on the Memphis square in front of my daddy's drugstore, hanging desperately to that cat. I couldn't even stop to say hello, but walked seven blocks home, where I fell into a bloody heap on our living room floor and let go. After that bad day, the cat avoided me like the plague, though I tried hard to make him love me.

My memory isn't all that bad, but the reason I have such a time recalling my cats' names is that my mother called them all "Fool." She wasn't fond of cats and she called them Gray Fool, White Fool, Black Fool, Orange Fool and those names became the cats' names, except for Grayling, that good cat.

All of those dogs and cats, and many I can't recall, died of untreated diseases and sudden strange spells, probably rabies. The coyotes were yipping every night down on the creek at the foot of Seventh Street, likely carrying rabies. None of our animals died of old age. There was no pet food; they ate what we ate. We buried them all in our cemetery, plus many other creatures. If we found a dead bird, we gave it a name, a stone, and a proper funeral. We even buried our horned toads; we called them "hornit toads." When they were pets, the horned toads died of bad diets, but they were buried in cigar boxes with prayers, songs, and stones for their names.

Those sweet creatures are lying there yet, in that vacant lot down on Seventh Street. It was still vacant the last time I saw it. The stones were gone.

THE WOLf AT THE DOOR

I love to talk about how poor we were during the Depression. I know my kids are tired of it, but I can't help it. It is the color and the smell of it that I can't get out of my mind.

It was brown, the color of dirt, even in Memphis on the edge of the dust bowl. We didn't have to go to California, couldn't have gone, in fact, having no car, much less a truck. But our old white house was four feet off the ground, with cracks in the floors and rattly windows. When the dust storms came, they would blow without end for many long, black, dark days.

We slept on the sleeping porch, a room with many beds and windows. Our front bedrooms were full of boarders. We woke up covered with dirt, with brown faces and gritty teeth. My mother's teeth were on edge. She was, in better days, a funny, cheerful woman, but in those brown days she was a witch with a very short temper.

She shouted us out of bed, shook the sheets, and came with a bucket of soap suds, which she poured on the old floors and swept out the back door. While she did this, we were shivering around, washing our faces, putting on our poor clothes and trying not to aggravate her. She fed us, somehow, and sent us to school with wet handkerchiefs tied over our noses. We walked through a wall of wind and sand to school, where we removed our handkerchiefs and sat all day with black eyes and white faces, looking like a bunch of raccoons.

During those times, we learned never to talk back to Ma. At least John and I did, but my sister Bob couldn't get the hang of it. We had a little room with a closet off the sleeping porch, and Bob would go in that closet and talk back. "Shut up, you crazy old woman," she would say. "I don't have to and you can't make me!" John and I, with ears pressed to the closet door, would whisper, "Say it again, Bob!"

We were not the poorest in Memphis; we were never hungry as many were, but we were the poorest among neighbors and friends we knew well. We didn't know that we were poor. My mother considered us exiled royalty on temporary hard times. The hard times were not temporary, but they weren't all bad. For one thing, they smelled like homemade bread. Our house was seldom rid of the heavenly, yeasty smell. Ma made wonderful bread, and sometimes, in a rare good mood, cinnamon rolls, dripping with caramelized brown sugar and butter.

I would take a loaf of bread and go fearfully to Mary King Martin's house down on the corner. She was a sister to the undertaker, and I knew that coffins were stored upstairs. The house was in a thicket of unkempt trees and brush; it was old, huge, and gray from lack of paint. It looked like the House of Usher. I knocked timidly on the back door, thankful to see Mary. Her red hair and smiling face didn't go with the house. She gave me a dime for the loaf. I took the dime to Mammy Franks, who gave me a gallon of milk for it. I sloshed home with the milk and Ma took the heavy cream off the top and made whipped butter in a little glass churn. We called it "cow butter." Spread on a piece of the bread, it was worth the fright of the trip to Mary's.

And then there was the hog's head. A friend with a farm would bring us one every fall. A huge head, it was laid out on the kitchen table. It was an exciting time for us and our friends as we gathered to stare at the great snout, bristly hairs and big blind eyes. Ma attacked that head with a large knife and reduced it to a bare skull, coloring herself and the table red. She cooked the brain and we had brains and eggs. She cooked the tongue and every little piece of pork that she could find. And she made hogshead cheese from the lips and other horrible things. I could never abide it. She baked the skin slowly until it became cracklin's. Cracklin's are kin to the little pork skins sold as snacks today, but not quite the same. Ma put them in cornbread; we called it cracklin' bread. I wish I had some.

About that time, gas was brought to Memphis and we acquired gas stoves for cooking and heating, and our pride and joy, a hot water tank. We had to light the fire under the tank and wait for it to heat, but not forget to turn it off after baths. Before the tank, we bathed in washtubs in the kitchen in winter, heating the water on our kerosene stove. Our bathroom faced the North Pole, and the winds blowing through it off the Great High Plains made it unbearable for bare, wet bodies.

One Saturday, my father left work early, and after we had all had a bath we went to the circus. Tom Mix, our favorite cowboy movie star, was there, racing around the ring on his big and famous white horse. We came home euphoric and opened the back door. We were met with steam and the smell of hot metal. "The tank! The tank!" my mother shouted as we ran for the bathroom. The tank was red hot and glowing. After that fright, we weren't so nervous about the tank. We had supposed, if we ever failed to turn it off, that it would blow our house to smithereens.

We had entertainments during the Depression other than the circus. Yankees would come to town and put out fliers inviting everyone to try out for a stupendous show. School kids got to be in the chorus. The show, mostly chorus, would be put on in the high school auditorium with tickets sold to everyone in town with fifty cents. The directors would then leave town with the money, but we had such fun we never noticed.

When I was thirteen, near Halloween, I was in a chorus line of ghosts. As we danced across the stage, singing ghost sounds, we were to raise our arms high. Unfortunately, I thought at that time that my skinny arms were too long for my body. I envied all the short, round arms. When the time came, at practice, to raise arms, I carefully raised mine to head level. The director would point at me and shout, "Get 'em up, get 'em up!" To me, having to raise my abnormally long arms in front of an audience was the low point of the Depression.

For the entertainments, whether they were shows put on by the out-of-towners or by the schools or just local dances, I wore a beautiful, yellow chiffon evening dress, loaned to me by Bob's friend, Ann Pallmeyer. I wore it for every occasion requiring a long dress after I was twelve. When I left in it for high school, to practice whatever, I would float all the way.

When I came home in the dark, I would dance down the sidewalks, spinning around the poles under the street lights, a glamorous yellow vision. That dress made me forget that my arms were too long.

The Norwegian painter Munch used yellow for anxiety, and yellow is the color of cowardice and caution, but to me it is a brave color, the color of happiness.

While my father was trying hard to save his drugstore (he didn't), my mother was up before five, making nine lunches for nine engineers who had come to Memphis to survey the Red River in one of Roosevelt's make-work programs. No matter what is said about such things, it saved their lives and ours. Two of them lived with their wives in our front bed-rooms. Seven had left their families behind. Ma filled the lunch sacks with big sandwiches of her good bread and what she had, sometimes homegrown tomatoes, a homemade pickle, an apple, and one of her famous fried apricot pies. And then they came to dinner and we all washed dishes.

When I was grown, it was all I could do to make two lunches for my daughters until they grew out of them. Getting up at five and making nine lunches would have killed me. And I doubt I would have gone to heaven, with my hateful thoughts. I could never cuss and shout like my mother did. Her cussing and shouting saved her.

We had a wolf at our door, but he was a glorious wolf. He came with our first boarder. Our first boarder, for supper, bed and breakfast, was the Wolf Brand Chili man, who came in a bright red car. Mounted on the right front fender was a large, real, stuffed wolf. His fierce green eyes glowed, his mouth was open in a snarl, his big, white teeth gleamed, ready to eat us.

Bob, John, and I waited in the yard to greet the boarder the first time he came. The Wolf man went in the house, but we never said a word, struck dumb in grand amazement. After that day we were celebrities. The wolf was our wolf. On the Wolf man's day, our yard filled with children, who would run at the wolf, shout at the wolf, growl at the wolf, but no child dared to touch him. At dark, Ma came out and sent them all home, leaving the poor old wolf in peace on his red fender.

The wolf at our door was the high point of the Depression, as I knew it.

OLD FRIENDS

We were old friends, even when we were young. The Depression made us older than we would have been. We became best friends in 1930. The oldest, I had just quit following my old gang around and playing with boys, when I began to play, day and night, with Jean and Jane. We knew how to play.

We thought ourselves the three musketeers, having seen the movie. Once we went on an exploration, with peanut butter sandwiches and Jane's little brother, Don Q. We knew Broom's Creek, which ran past the foot of Seventh Street, with its cliffs and woods, but on that day we went where we had never been. We went down a pretty little draw, or creek, that crossed our side street on its way to the gins and the railroad tracks. We had made things of the clay dug from the bank under the bridge, but we had never wondered where it went, until that day. We walked down that draw, hoping to discover something, until it disappeared into a bleak, brown, empty countryside. We walked on forever. There was no need for a look of wild surmise. We found nothing on our first grand expedition into an unknown wilderness. There was no wilderness, just an empty place, as some places are in West Texas. As Gertrude Stein said, "There was no there, there." It was a long way home. Don Q. cried every step of the way.

When I began to play with Winifred Jane Tarver and Jean Denny, we were obsessed with play. We played morning, noon, and night in the summer and winter afternoons until dark, when two of us were sent home, unless we spent the night.

We played paper dolls, cutting out people from the fashion pages of women's magazines. We haunted the dry goods store at the end of the season for pattern books. You can't play paper dolls properly with celebrity paper dolls, sold in bookstores, with their punch-out clothes. The lives of those dolls have already been lived.

Real paper dolls have new lives and you need a magazine to hold them. You write the names of a mother, father, and children at the tops of the first pages. Then you collect many figures of the proper age and size for each person. When a change of clothes is required, you simply take a new doll from that person's supply. Faces are ignored; these are seen in the mind's eye. Paper furniture is made and rooms with imaginary walls are spread all over the floor. Your paper doll children grow up and marry the children from other magazines. Ours never divorced; we knew nothing of that. After a year or so, your magazine will be crammed with extended families, who will have endured all of the joy and sorrow that a young girl can know, first hand or from movies. I imagine that the person who wrote the first soap opera had played paper dolls.

We played "movie star" in the Denny's storm cellar. We hung out down there, reading movie magazines. There were a lot of old clothes there, and we would dress up in the old taffeta dresses and play the game. "Who is your favorite movie star?" "Joan Crawford. Bette Davis." First to say the name got to be the star. When we came to the male category, we all said, "Ronald Reagan!" I wasn't fond of Ronald as a president, but he once was my favorite movie star.

Movies were everything to us. After seeing *Treasure Island*, we buried a treasure. We each put one of our most treasured possessions in a cigar box and buried it, making an elaborate map of its location. We agreed to wait until we could forget the place. Then we traced off the steps and dug. We counted steps and dug holes all day. What kind of a lowdown, dirty, no-good rat would have stolen our treasure? I still look for the scoundrel.

Jean lived in an old Victorian house full of women. She lived with her grandmother, widowed mother, widowed aunt, cousin, and old maid aunt, Ida Mae. Ida Mae was the telephone operator. In Memphis, when you took the receiver off its hook and spoke into the mouthpiece, you didn't say "104-J," even if you knew the number. You said, "Ida Mae, get me Aint Gussie." Ida Mae knew every voice in town.

The most interesting thing in that old house of women, built before bathrooms, was its upstairs commode. At the head of the stairs was a long hall, passing the bedrooms. It ended at a little window that reached to the floor. Next to that window was the commode, exposed to the back yard, whether the window was open or closed. It was no place to spend any time, with your head jerking left to the yard and right to the stairs.

Jean's old grandma, Gram, was the ruler. She went through the house making loud, scoffing sounds and was always scolding us. But on cold, snowy days, she made fudge and popcorn.

When we were painting our fingernails with stolen polish, she would sneak up and say in a low, horrible voice, "Dripping blood!"

Jean's cousin, June, who lived with her mother upstairs, took tap-dancing; she idolized Ginger Rogers. Over our play noise and Gram's grumbling was the constant sound of June's tap shoes on the old wooden floor above, *tap, tappity, tap,* twice, then *tap, brush, tap, brush, STOMP.* We often played "Chopsticks" loudly on their upright piano to drown her out. June would shout down the stairs, "Cut it out!"

To June, we were three pains-in-the-neck. We constantly spied on her. She would come home from high school with her beau, Tom Bob. Tom Bob would chase her around the back yard, and they would roll in the grass, Tom Bob tickling her while she shrieked at the top of her voice. And they *kissed.* All the while we would be watching, thrilled, from the cellar, or the bushes, or the upstairs hall, our heads in the window under the commode. I don't know if Ginger Rogers ever rolled in the grass with a boy, but June was Ginger to us.

Jean was what we called "spoiled." When she was asked to wear the matching bloomers for a homemade dress, she chose, instead, a pair of silk ones. A huge fight ensued. She locked herself in the bathroom, put the stoppers in the tub and lavatory, turned the water on full force, and began to beat on the door with a pair of shoes, screaming at the top of her voice. This scared me, as it would never have happened at my house. I said to Gram, Jean's mother, and her aunts, who were all involved in the dispute, "I have to go home now, my mother wants me." I never knew how that problem was resolved. I left them all shouting over Jean's screams. The house of women was a house of noise.

Winifred Jane, who became Janie, lived with her parents, brother, and grandparents in the grandparents' home. It was more modern, a grand house. It had a winding stairway, and at its foot in a beautiful living room, was a grand piano. The year I took music lessons, I practiced on it. My mother had made a large, embroidered, cut-work tablecloth with twelve napkins for my lessons.

I was about four months into those lessons and had not learned to read music, when I was murdering a little piece on that piano. Janie's lovely grandmother came and stood behind me. "Child," she said, "do you know middle C?" "No, Ma'am," I said. She pointed it out and put her finger on it and said that every note up is with your right hand, every note down is with your left, and she demonstrated it for me. "When you are lost," she said, "come back to middle C." Suddenly, I read that music. Ever since that day, when I don't know up from down, I say to myself, "Child, do you know middle C?"

I thought that the Tarvers were the most elegant people in the world. Janie looked like her handsome father. She had gray-green eyes and sandy hair, and in the summer, when she was tan, her hair, eyes, and skin seemed to be all the same color. I loved the look. They had an elegant house, elegant ways, and elegant food. I ate the first fresh-shelled English peas I ever saw at their table. Our only fresh peas were black-eyed; the English ones were from a can. Once on a golden afternoon at sundown, we floated around in their boat on a little lake, and Mrs. Tarver served us an elegant picnic with "foie gras," goose liver pâté from France. "This is real life," I said to myself.

On winter afternoons, Mrs. Tarver sat on a couch in her upstairs bedroom reading books before an open fire. I thought it the grandest thing to do, and I vowed to myself that when I grew up, I would sit before a fire reading books in the afternoon. I kept the vow.

On their driveway was a big, creamy yellow roadster with a rumble seat. I think of it as a Buick. I don't know what it was, but Janie could drive it. We would get in, heads barely visible, and

Janie, with tiny arms and no power steering, would wheel that monster off the end of the driveway into the side street, make a U-turn, then left on Sixth and back into the driveway. Round and round we would go, until her mother shouted, "Winifred Jane! Get out of that car!" But, oh, it was fun while it lasted.

Someone said, "Old friends are soon parted," and so it was. All good things must end. When we went to high school, I was a year ahead and we took up with different "bunches." In high school, your bunch is all.

Once, on the way home from a football game in a school bus, I was wondering where Jean was, when I saw out the window an open convertible passing the bus. Jean was in the back seat, all entwined with one of the handsomest boys that ever lived. She married him right out of high school. The last time I ever saw her, nearly fifty years ago, she was sitting in the swing on the porch of Gram's house with a beautiful little boy. Jean died very young of cancer. I heard that her husband killed himself. She was so beautiful. I think he died of a broken heart. Winifred Jane married an architect. She lives in Kansas and is a college professor, teaching, naturally, art history. She came to see me once in the early fifties. I haven't seen her since, but we write and she sends me pictures of her large, and, of course, elegant family.

I have had in this world many acquaintances and some close friends. I have had five or six of the close ones for nearly fifty years. If I called, they would come. But childhood friends are a different breed. They are old friends, most often never seen again, but they live in your mind as children, bright-eyed and beautiful. You know nothing of their growing old, their mistakes, their sorrows, or their dying. I have had my old friends in my heart, along with golden afternoons, popcorn, fudge, and foie gras, for sixty-five years. I love them still.

DEPRIVATIONS AND
SEASONAL TRAUMAS

I never had a Shirley Temple doll. The year my two old friends got theirs, I got a little doll about twelve inches high. She didn't have real hair, but she had a sweet face. I loved playing with her when I was alone, but when she was with Shirley, she was plain and pale and wan. My old friends were good friends, though, and they let me play with their new dolls.

Shirley was big and beautiful, with her dimples, real hair, real skin, and she had a little round belly. "Just like a real stomach," we said. My stomach didn't look anything like Shirley's; I didn't have one. "Oh well," I told myself, "you're older than Shirley, too skinny and too old to have a round stomach." I have one, now. Be careful what you wish for.

My old friends had skates when I didn't. I learned to skate on theirs. The Christmas I got skates, they got red scooters. I skated around after them on their scooters, but they were good friends and let me ride them. However, we preferred to skate. I never was that fond of scooters.

We made a big thing of Christmas at our house. I still do in mine. Early in the fall we began to raise money. My mother worked downtown in the dry goods store on Saturdays. She made fudge, which my sister Bob, when she was too young to work downtown, took in sacks to sell at the gins and the cottonseed mill down by the railroad tracks. It wasn't a good place for a child to be, but it was safe enough in those days. My brother John delivered circulars and newspapers, walking with a pack on his back, having no bicycle.

I baby-sat two young girls all day on Saturday while their mother worked. I gave them lunch and naps, and played with them until I was bored out of my skull, for twenty-five cents.

When I was twelve, I was working for $1.50 every Saturday until Christmas for Old Man Wherry in his jewelry and variety store. I worked all day until closing time, which might be eleven o'clock. Bob had done the same at my age, but by the time I worked for Mr. Wherry, she was selling clothes afternoons and Saturdays for the Rosenwasser brothers, who had the only high fashion store in town. However, she spent most of her income on clothes. She was mad about clothes. She still is.

At Mr. Wherry's, I mainly sold bay rum to a stream of steady customers. Bay rum was an after-shave, with a spicy smell and lots of alcohol. My customers would be the homeless today, but we knew none then. These men weren't hobos; they were our local alcoholics. They simply couldn't afford bootlegger prices.

We had no fireplace, but we hung our stockings on nails driven into the wall behind our pot-bellied, coal-burning stove. The stockings were filled with nuts, apples, oranges, and candy. They held no surprises, as stockings do today. (A daughter of mine once found a car key in hers.) Those nails were there year round, even after the stove was gone. One summer night, when that old stove was still there, our cousins were spending the night and we hung some stockings on the nails, hoping to confuse Santa. My mother filled them with coal and switches.

"Oh well, nice try," we said.

We were in the Methodist church every Christmas Eve. Parents brought trinkets for their children, so that every child would have something off the tree. There were extra presents for those whose parents could bring nothing. Every child got a sack of candy, and we sang "Joy to the World" at the tops of our voices.

The best Christmas Eve of my childhood was in that lovely old church. That day, my mother sent my sister Loisie to the hardware store to get something for me at the last minute. "Take it to the church and wait for us," she said. Loisie bought me a real porcelain tea set with many, many pieces—charging it, of course. The dishes were translucent white with blue borders and, except for big things like bicycles, it was the most expensive item for a child in the store. At church, the names were called as the children received their gifts, and when I went for mine it was too big for me to carry to my seat. My mother moaned.

We walked home with that big box in the cold, crystal-clear night. Venus was like the great Christmas star in the sky, hanging near a sliver of a moon. And I thought to myself, "Joy to the world, there really is a Santa Claus."

But the bicycle thing nearly killed me. I was eight years old, too old to believe in Santa Claus, but I was the baby and I pretended, because I knew that it pleased us all. We had the biggest tree we could afford, and we decorated it very early and tenderly. We put the big, hot lights on it, our old decorations, and then the tinsel. The tinsel was a heavy, leady stuff that we saved from year to year. We smoothed it and hung it methodically on every branch until it reached the top, gleaming in all of its glory. We children sat around that awesome tree every night until Christmas Eve, playing carols on our old Victrola, and wondering. We put our meager presents around it. We had eggnog and opened them on Christmas morning. My mother made wonderful eggnog of egg whites, beaten until stiff, the yellows beaten with thick cream, a little sugar, and a lot of bourbon. We children had a cup, bourbon and all. I needed it on the morning that I did not get my bicycle.

We didn't have enough rooms for the people in our house, especially with boarders or company, and we slept wherever we could find a spot. That Christmas Eve, the night before I didn't get my bicycle, I was to sleep with my daddy in a front bedroom, off the living room. My daddy said, "Now close your eyes, and I will carry you to bed for fear Santa might be near." Of course I peeped, and as he lugged my skinny eight-year-old body through our big, old living room, I glimpsed the handlebars . . . of a red scooter.

I was a child who had learned to appreciate whatever came my way, so I didn't cry all night. But I wanted to.

My old friends, of course, got bicycles that Christmas morning and I raced around after them on my scooter. They were good friends, though, and taught me to ride their bicycles, giving me many turns on them.

I never had a bicycle until my husband gave me a beautiful white Schwinn for my forty-fifth birthday in 1969. I rode that bicycle like the wind all over Houston for years.

I still have a bicycle, though I am seventy. Sometimes, when I am feeling old and sad, I ride my bicycle, not up, but down the hills in Lakeway. When I race down these hills, with the wind whipping my old gray head, I am eight years old again.

And I *want* a Shirley Temple doll.

READING IN THE SCHOOL Of HARD KNOCKS

A long, long time ago, when no one called ahead or even knocked, Mammy Franks, a sweet old woman, came from the porch into the front bedroom, where I was in bed with the flu. I was reading. To be in bed alone in that room was heaven. In our house, to have a room of one's own required a contagious disease. Mammy was smiling sweetly until her ancient eyes rested on my book. She gave a loud snort and shouted for my mother. My mother ran through the house, frightened. I had been near death the year before, and she kept a wary eye on me. Mammy yelled, "She is reading . . . (gasp) . . . She is reading *Anthony Adverse!*" "Yes, isn't that wonderful," said Ma on her way to the kitchen. "And she's only nine years old!"

I don't recall that *Anthony Adverse* was shocking, but it does seem that something strange went on in a ditch. If so, I wanted to know what it was. Nine-year-old girls were far more innocent and ignorant than they are today. Or maybe it wasn't in a ditch. (My memory is as ancient as were Mammy's eyes.) Wherever, I loved it. I skipped the words that I didn't know, but I *was* reading a bestseller in the days when the slightest hint of sex made old women snort and shout.

In the second grade I had pneumonia, a terrible thing to have before antibiotics, and I missed the second semester. I really didn't miss it. I surpassed it, reading in bed all day through the spring and afternoons all summer. For six long months, "I was the giant great and still that sits upon the pillow hill, and sees before him dale and plain, the pleasant land of counterpane." I didn't play with leaden soldiers, but I knew the poem, thought myself the giant, and made crude little animals and people of clay to play out their stories on my old quilt.

We were pitifully poor, but exceedingly rich. It was the best of times, it was the worst of times, maybe or maybe not the age of wisdom, but it was the age of foolishness, when I grew up in a house full of books in the worst of the Depression. I had this great advantage in Memphis, Texas, out in the Red River Valley on the Prairie Dog Fork of the Red at the foot of the Palo Duro Canyon, where no one had ever seen or heard of a bookstore.

*   *   *   *   *

I also had Miss Grace Ezzell. Miss Grace Ezzell taught us all to read in the first grade. She was a tiny woman, not a head taller than any of us. She had a deformed hip and lurched around the room, teaching phonetics with a ruler, whacking and prodding as we read "See Spot Run" and much, much more. If the big boys snickered or balked, she dragged them into the cloak room and whipped them unmercifully. I do not know how she did it—they were twice her size—but she reduced them to sniveling pulps. They were then glad to say, in very weak voices, the sounds of pain: A - Ah! O - Oh! U - ooh! In her class, you either learned to read or you were killed. None of us died.

She sounds like an ogre, but her blue eyes were always smiling and she had the sweetest voice. She came from Quitique, a little place not far from Memphis on the Caprock Canyon, and she stopped off in Weatherford, where she taught Mary Martin to read. I have always felt a kinship with Mary Martin, knowing that she learned the sounds of A, E, I, O and U from Grace Ezzell.

Grace worshipped vowels, and I've always wondered what she would have done with Arthur Rimbaud and his poem about the secret origins of the vowels. He said that they came from color— A noir, E blanc, I rouge, U vert, O bleu. In those colors, he saw death, purity, laughter of beautiful lips, spit blood, dark green oceans, the wonder of wrinkles on old readers' foreheads, and a harsh trumpet sound in silences crossed by worlds and by angels.

Miss Grace Ezzell's small, warped body was not worthy of her great soul. Wherever she is in the great beyond, I see her tall and having a lot of fun with Rimbaud.

For years she had collected children's picture books. She kept them in a little library off her kitchen. In the summer after our first grade, we went once a week, sat on her porch with punch and cookies and read aloud from those books. Most of the children in those poor times had no books at home, and if they didn't come for Miss Ezzell's Saturday salon, they were sent for. I loved her books because we had no picture books in our house. My father thought that Robert Louis Stevenson sufficed. He told us Peter Rabbit and Uncle Remus stories and thought that we could find plenty to read in his grown-up books. Miss Ezzell allowed us to take as many books home as we could read, but woe to the child who brought them back unread.

In the fall after my first summer with her books, she had a kitchen fire and the books were burned and wet beyond repair. When I saw those burned books, I ran out into her back yard, fell to the ground, and threw a squalling fit. O, Bleu!

* * * * *

Until I went to school, I thought that the Uncle Remus stories were my daddy's own; I thought that Brer Rabbit lived in the woods at Kosse, where my daddy was born. When I was about four, I rode through those woods in the back of a wagon. The woods then were dark and deep, the trees intertwined over the old dirt road, the only sounds the horse's hoofs and birds. My eyes and ears strained for a glimpse or a whisper of Brer Bar or Brer Fox. My daddy told us these tales as if they had actually happened up in the old Kosse woods when he was a child, and he mesmerized us with them, night after night. I know that he read them, though he loved us thinking they were his.

Joel Chandler Harris's first book of Uncle Remus stories came out in 1880, the year before my daddy was born. And I find it the strangest thing that some of the myths and plots in those stories were also told by the Indians in the Amazon. Harris noted that Herbert Smith, studying the myths and folklore of Brazil, found a story of the tortoise outrunning the deer, identical to Brer Tarrypin and Brer Rabbit. Smith also traced tales to India and Siam, some to Egypt, some to American

Indians. But he found that the Amazonian tales bore the greatest resemblance to our Uncle Remus. I can imagine that these essentially African tales got into the Amazon when slaves were taken to Brazil, and were spread through those vast jungles just as my daddy passed them on to me.

I went up the Amazon River not long ago, and as I hiked into the rain forests, I thought of the old Kosse woods, now gone, and listened for a glimpse or a whisper. There are wonderful mysteries in this world.

My favorite story was one about Uncle Remus cooking a possum and sweet potatoes. While he was nodding over his fire, Brer Fox or one of the other scoundrels came and ate the possum and potatoes, smearing Uncle Remus's nose and mouth with bits of them. Uncle Remus woke up, found his food gone, with the taste in his mouth. "The taste is dar, the smell is dar, but the feeling ain't dar," he said, rubbing his stomach. I mutter those old words to myself even today, when I am suspicious of health care promises from Washington, or when some developer tells us the great things in store for our creeks. "The taste is dar, the smell is dar, but the feeling ain't dar." My gut knows.

*   *   *   *   *

My daddy was a Reader with a capital "R." When he felt the urge for a little Shakespeare, he didn't skim around in "Hamlet" recalling movies, as most of us with the same urge do. He read the whole thing, all of Shakespeare, from first play to last. He read all of Dickens, Emerson, Scott, Kipling, Burns, Stevenson, Poe, Proust, Eliot (George and T.S.), and Lord knows what else. He read them many times. He read and owned them all. He read the *Fort Worth Star Telegram*, *The Dallas Morning News*, and the *Denver Post*, all brought to Memphis on the early morning trains and thrown into our yard by little boys on bicycles. At the edge of hunger, we had *Harper's*, *Atlantic Monthly*, *The Saturday Evening Post*, *Colliers*, *Life*, and the *Saturday Review of Literature*.

We also had some bad scrapes with bill collectors. "Mr. Lindsey would have cut off the water today if I hadn't chased him out of the yard," my mother said one day to my daddy. *"Do not bring one more book into this house!"* He ordered most of his books in sets and had barrister bookcases which came in sections. After her ultimatum, he smuggled the books in one at a time and stashed them around, as alcoholics do bottles. When he knew that she was to be away for an afternoon, he would bring in a new bookcase section and gather in his books. My mother never seemed to notice that the bookcases grew to cover all the walls in our living room. Or at least she pretended not to, but she was also a reader.

My daddy read *Oliver Twist* to me and my brother John when we were very small. Perched on the arms of his chair, we would soon want to get down. *Oliver Twist* always made us hungry. He kept us by promising us a "puff" from his cigar. Engrossed in the story, he forgot his cigar, and John and I passed it back and forth, puffing happily away. I gave up cigars after *Oliver Twist* and *David Copperfield*, but I don't know about John. My mother and I, walking far from home (always walking since we had no car), once met John delivering circulars when he was twelve. He didn't see us until we were face to face. He was smoking a big, black cigar. Ma snatched the cigar and stomped it to smithereens, then walked on without saying a word. She never did say anything about it, but John lived in fear and trembling for weeks.

* * * * *

In the very pit of the Depression, I came home from school one day and said that my geography teacher wanted us to have a fifty-cent workbook. "Is she mad?!" my mother asked. "There isn't fifty cents in this town. No." The next day, I brought home the bad news that if I didn't have the workbook, I could only make a "C." Ma said, "You tell that red-headed witch that if you get a 'C,' I will come to school and kill her!" Someone finally moved away and I inherited a workbook for twenty-five cents, which Ma reluctantly sent. Though I thought she would make good her threat, I never reported a word of it to the teacher. It was a lesson in diplomacy. It was also a lesson in parental involvement, much easier in those old days. My mother had known the red-headed witch since the day she was born.

Ma swapped cut-work and other embroidery to Mrs. Harrison for "expression" lessons. We memorized great poems and recited them "with feeling" for a crowd in the third-floor auditorium at West Ward, the old and only elementary school for white children in Memphis. Once, at Christmas, Mrs. Harrison had taught my sister Bob a long, beautiful poem suitable for a twelve-year-old girl. But Bob, the original rebel, chose instead a short poem from our little blue books, *The World's 101 Best Poems*. It was about a little boy who didn't like to wash his hands. She recited the last lines in her best little boy voice, "I guess when I die and go flying through the sky, God will holler out and say, 'Son, did you wash?!'" Poor Mrs. Harrison slumped back in her chair and even my mother, whom nothing surprised, looked startled.

* * * * *

Memphis had a Carnegie Library, a beautiful little Georgian building, two stories high, on the edge of a pretty park with a bandstand. In the summer I would hang out there with my teenage friends, trooping up and down the stairs, looking for love stories. We would stop off in the bandstand and lounge around, reading aloud the spicy passages. The Carnegie had the latest books, straight from New York. We felt so smug and intellectual when we read those books.

I went back to Memphis in 1970 when we buried my father in the old cemetery. I found two noble, elegant old churches gone, replaced by low, nondescript buildings. One had been next to the Carnegie, one across the street. The Taj Mahal replaced by a strip center. The Carnegie Library was gone. They had taken it down because "it no longer served its purpose." It would have served as a Monument to Reading. There was only an ugly blank place where it had been, and the sight of it left an ugly blank place in my heart. I wanted to fall to the ground and throw a squalling fit.

*   *   *   *   *

I have my mother's old composition book. Brown with age, nearly a hundred years old, the pages are crumbling away. Her name is on its cover—Key Ayers, age 15. Inside are many questions.

On a page titled *Civil Government:* What is a poll tax? What is an indirect tax? Give a brief account of the Constitution and grand juries. What is the extent of the jurisdiction of the Justice of the Peace, as to the amount of money involved, as to the character of the crime charged? What is Congress? From what source does it derive its power? Discuss the Fifteenth Amendment. (The Fifteenth Amendment, adopted in 1870, seventeen years before my mother was born, ordered federal and state governments not to keep any citizen from voting because of race or color. It did not mention gender. I wonder what she said about it.) From what source are the available school funds derived? What does the state's annual proportion yield?

Unfortunately, there are no answers in my mother's little book. She had to stand and deliver them in school. Ninety-two years later, I can't answer some of those questions. Nobody yet knows the answer to the last one.

There are pages of history questions in the book. There is a half page of science, the parts of the brain and speculations about thought. There are pages of grammar rules, but there is no math. My mother taught school for a year when she was about nineteen, but she had to give it up because she didn't have enough arithmetic. She did know how to add, subtract, and multiply. My father, probably because he was a male, learned much more. He was a pharmacist in the days when he had to grind and weigh powders, measure liquids, and make his own medicine from precise formulas.

Most of the pages in this now ancient composition book are filled with great classic poems. I have searched for one of them in my oldest books of quotations and all of my old books of poetry. I can't find it, but it sounds like Poe or Longfellow or maybe Tennyson. Whoever, it seems to speak to me today, sums up our temporary tragedies, and I can almost see her, with her coal-black eyes and straight black Indian hair, so beautiful and dramatic, reciting its last stanzas in that old wooden schoolhouse in the center of Texas, so long ago:

> *As the moon glitters coldly alone,*
> *Above the earth on her cloud-woven throne,*
> *As the rocky bound cave repulseth a wave,*
> *So thy anger repulseth me.*
>
> *As the bitter black frost of a night,*
> *Stays the roses with pitiless might,*
> *As a sharp dagger thrust hurls a king to the dust,*
> *So thy cruelty murdereth me.*

My mother never knew any real cruelty, except for her terrible poverty and that her mother died in childbirth with her ninth child, the same year that she filled my old book with poetry and learned it by heart.

She had magnificent eyes, inherited from a Cherokee grandmother. They could look into your very soul. I see her eyes today in Pablo Neruda's beautiful poem, "Widower's Tango." In the poem, there is a woman named Maligna. Maligna had a swallow, sleeping and flying, living in her eyes. But she harbored a mad dog in her heart. My mother's eyes were mostly swallows, but when she was pushed too far by her poverty and people who would not do the right thing, her mad dog would come up into her eyes and look out. You wouldn't want to be around when that happened, unless you could stand a quivering chill that reached right down from your eyes through the pit of your stomach to your toes.

* * * * *

My mother and daddy went to public school. After graduation, she went to "Normal" for a year and he apprenticed to a pharmacist. They were educated people. They were educated, a hundred years ago, by reading, copying and reciting great poetry. They revered poetry all of their lives. They revered poets. They revered reading. They were born poor and died poor. They never had a cent, never owned a car, never owned a house, never went to college, yet they were educated because of their great love of reading. It was all that I inherited. I would not take a billion for it.

Benjamin Franklin, on being asked what condition of man he considered the most pitiable, said, "A lonesome man on a rainy day who does not know how to read." It would be a pitiable day for any of us. To be unable to read must be the saddest thing on this good earth. The second saddest thing must be to be able, but *not* to read.

I am growing old, but I will be a reader until the day I die. When I do, I hope I don't go to what my mother called "the bad place." I call it "Hell" and am afraid they stoke the fires with books down there. Until it is decided where I will go, I will work on my education, for all who read for pleasure and knowledge are educated.

Those who do, are. Them who don't, ain't. And those who *can* but *don't* are almost certain to go to the bad place.

FRED CLARK AND KATE

My mother often told us about the day that she decided to marry my daddy. She was standing with her sister on an old, red-dirt road that went through the woods at Eutaw on its way to Kosse. She had coal-black hair and big, black eyes. She was dirty and was drawing a picture in the dust with her big toe when he rode by, shining clean and handsome, on his horse. Actually, I made that up about her drawing a picture in the dust with her toe, but she was barefooted. And she did draw. She once drew a picture of a little black girlfriend and put it on the gate. Her little friend, recognizing herself in the unflattering portrait, beat the stuffing out of her. She was twelve years old the day my daddy rode by. He didn't notice her, but she watched him galloping away and said, "I will marry that man."

She called him Fred when she spoke to him, but when she referred to him or was mad, which was every day, she called him Fred Clark. He never called her Kate; he called her "Lady."

They were teetotally incompatible.

She came from the McDaniels and McKinleys, and she lived in a little house in Eutaw, the ruins of a town her great-grandfather and his Cherokee bride had settled. The great-grandfather, Charles Carson McKinley, supposedly came to Texas in disgrace for having married an Indian. Her name was Nancy Wallace. I wish I knew why; it seems to me a strange name for an Indian woman. The truth is that they came with children and grand-children. His name is on a historical marker on Highway 7 near Kosse. Hers is not.

Fred was the son of the doctor and lived in a big, two-storied house across the road. The doctor had four children and was a farmer when he decided to become a doctor. He went to Tulane for one year, learned all they knew in those days, came home and hung out his shingle. He kept two horses, one hitched to his buggy, and one standing by. Fred's mother's name was Julia. That is all that I know about her, except for Kate's daughter-in-law remarks, that Julia sat, dressed-up, on the porch all the time and did no housework. Not likely. All of my grandparents were dead before I was born. When Kate was fifteen, her mother died in childbirth with her ninth child, attended by Dr. Clark. It was the first time that he had used ether for pain. They named the baby Clark.

She often said that the reason Fred Clark didn't have a lick of common sense was because his folks hired a young black boy to look after him. On Saturday, she said, the boy would draw his bath, lay out his clothes, dress him, put him on his horse, aim it toward Kosse and give it a whack. And, she always added, the horse would bring him home, drunker than a skunk. But she married him anyhow. And there they were.

Kate was fearless. She loved storms and tempted tornadoes, never going to the cellar. She was loud, and she cursed when aggravated, which was often. She slammed around the house barefooted, cleaning and cooking wonderful food in an old shift she called her "housedress." She wore no bra or slip except for church and social occasions, the Missionary Society or the Delphians.

She was forever digging in the dirt, planting flowers, vegetables, and anything she could beg or borrow. She attracted people like flies; our house was always filled with friends, neighbors, and strangers. Before addresses, someone once asked for directions to our house and was told to go down Seventh Street until he reached a big, old, white house with every shade raised and every light on. But don't worry, he was told, you will hear it from two blocks away.

She was called on for all neighborhood disasters. Late one cold night, a woman came and said that there was a baby crying under her house. I remember shivering in the dark with the crowd that gathered. Kate crawled under the house with a flashlight. After a lot of thumping and bumping and cursing, a tomcat ran out. The men said that, oh, they would have gone under, but for fear that it really was a baby. She said, "Oh, hell, you cowards are scared of snakes and spiders!"

She had absolutely no patience. "The preacher preaches too long," she said one Sunday morning. "I'm leaving at noon." She sat on the aisle in the third row with neighbors to her left. Fred, usually late, sat in the back. At twelve sharp she left. Unfortunately, when she stood the neighbors also stood and opened their hymnals, looking at the preacher, who, after a slight pause and a hard stare, was still preaching. They were so chagrined at being caught not listening that they came after church threatening to kill her. She was still laughing when her chicken was done.

Fred, on the other hand, was a quiet, dignified, formal man, the soul of patience. He was kind and cheerful, and if he ever raised his voice or said a curse word, I don't recall it. He was afraid of storms, the first in the cellar in tornado times. He was incapable of housework or yardwork. He not only wore a starched white shirt, tie, and suit every day, but he didn't take them off until he went to bed. He was a pharmacist, but he wanted to write. He wrote letters to editors, kept a journal, and was a "liner" for the *Dallas Morning News,* sending little paragraphs from Memphis that were used as fillers. The only one I can remember is a story about a fight between a sparrow and a grasshopper in the dustbowl days. The grasshopper won.

Fred had no sense for business or money. "Lady," he would say, "I don't know what you are going to do, but I can't pay this." Kate took over the bill-paying after chasing Mr. Lindsey out of the yard when he came to cut off our water.

He saw good in everything. No matter where he lived, or under what miserable circumstances, like Candide, he saw it as the best of all possible worlds. "Come out," he would say, "and look at this glorious sky!" The glorious sky would be an ominous blood-red sun going down in a high cloud of boiling red dirt that would turn to black as it approached, changing day to night for three days.

He did hunt, his only manly thing. He went with his old double-barreled shotgun on a Sunday morning at dawn, down past the creek to Broom's Park, our woods. He came back, after waking the south end of town, with a bag of doves. Kate served them fried with biscuits and gravy for breakfast, and we were all in the Methodist Church at eleven.

His basic problem was reading. He bought and read every book he could get his hands on and haunted our Carnegie Library. He read poetry, novels, plays, magazines, newspapers; he read constantly, disappearing into literature to hide from a world that he never understood. In fact, the reason that he was in West Texas to begin with was that he read Horatio Alger's *Go West, Young Man*. He went to Lubbock when it was barely there, which should tell us something. He read with a grand, absent mind, oblivious to the poverty and the wild life that surrounded him. He was the most absent-minded man conceivable. He came and went with a book under his arm, like people go with briefcases, for fear that he would be caught somewhere with nothing to read.

When nudity still shocked, Mrs. Cypert, a country woman who had moved to our block and had never had a phone, was using ours one morning. In the hall opposite the bathroom, it was mounted high on the wall, and on a long cord it had a receiver which must have weighed three pounds. No wonder the teenage telephone syndrome had not yet evolved. Mrs. Cypert was shouting into the phone, could have been heard in Amarillo, when Fred came out of the bathroom bare-naked in search of his underwear. Mrs. Cypert screamed and ran out the back door, shrieking over and over, *"Oh dear Lord Jesus!"* She threw the receiver and left it swinging and banging around against the wall, a terrible din. Fred proceeded to his room with Kate charging after him. "Fred Clark, what have you done to Miz Cypert?!" "Mrs. Cypert?" he vaguely asked. "Do you mean to stand there stark nekkid and tell me that you didn't see or hear Miz Cypert on the phone?! God help us all!"

He never disciplined us. That was her job. He did attempt, once, to switch Bob, when she was very small. She got herself a switch and they revolved in a circle, exchanging blows. At breakfast one morning, Fred said, "Lady, when I left work last night, John was hanging around on the square with some boys. I wish that you would speak to him." "Hello, John," she said, with her terrible sarcasm. Late one night, after her curfew, Bob was on the front porch kissing the living daylights out of Droopy Drawers Hightower. Kate reached out and slapped her. Droop jumped over the banister into a giant lilac bush, and that poor boy was not only scared, he was scratched from end to end.

This same boy was crouched down once, stealing chicken that Kate was frying in the basement of the Methodist church, when he stood up and she swung a plate at the same time. The plate broke on his head, with blood and all. She said that she didn't mean to hurt him. Droop, whose name is Harold, is a dentist in Midland or somewhere. Wherever, I hope he hasn't lost his hair, exposing his scar.

She could criticize Fred, but we, the children, could not. She would say, "My God, Fred Clark has bought another set of books! We will starve to death!" Or, "My God, Fred Clark has bought another suit. Does he think he's a senator?!" We would chime in. "Why are we the only people in town without a car? We have to walk everywhere through rain and snow unless our friends pick us up. And our clothes are so tacky." "Shut up that whining," she would say. "How many of your friends have the Britannica and all of these blamed books? Be glad that your daddy doesn't lie or steal and that he will never shame you. And besides, he looks like a senator."

When they were passing middle age, they moved from Memphis in the Red River Valley to Lubbock on the Great High

Plains. She moved. He followed. The only sad thing about that move was that we left our Victrola and our records behind. We had dozens of records—big, heavy disks. Kate loved tenors and we had Caruso and her favorite, the Irish tenor John McCormack. When she was homesick or put-upon too much, she would wind up that old Victrola and play over and over his song, "I will take you home again, Kathleen." That old song makes me sad.

After losing John McCormack, she made do with singing "Amazing Grace" when she was sad or homesick. And another old hymn, which I have forgotten and cannot find, but when overwhelmed with work, she would boom out with it. "Keep your hand upon the throttle and your eye upon the rail." I still try to. We stayed out of the kitchen when we heard her singing.

After Memphis, Fred thought that Lubbock was paradise. He worked downtown in a drugstore for a while, and then became the pharmacist at a hospital, making his first living wage. He worked there until he was too old, and even then he worked in drugstores in the country outside of Lubbock, commuting by bus. He worked until he was eighty-two and never saved a dime. He drank whiskey and smoked cigars and would take a cab to the liquor store. Lubbock was as dry as a bone, but there was a little wet strip south of town. He would have the cab driver let him out on his driveway at the back porch, so the neighbors wouldn't see his whiskey sacks.

One day in Lubbock, after one of our many moves, he got off the bus and accidentally went into the house next door. Used to seeing strangers in our living room, he walked past a Texas Tech professor and his wife in theirs, clear back to the kitchen before he realized his error. On hearing about this, Kate asked, "What in the world did they say?" "Say?" said Fred.

"Why, they said not a word, nor did I, but I tipped my hat to them when I left." Never without his hat, he called it his "sky-piece." He could never find it, always asking, "Where is my sky-piece?"

While in Memphis, after our brother Freddy died, Kate became louder and meaner; Fred quieter and kinder. At that time, they went their separate ways. But they went their separate ways together. Had Fred Clark and Kate been born in the twenties, they might have divorced. Had they been born in the forties, they certainly would have. When he died at ninety in 1971, they had been married sixty-three years. Kate had seven great ones as a widow.

It is said that parents always at odds have a dire effect on their children. We have not been particularly crazy, but we are somewhat eccentric. Bob and I have a horrible addiction to newspapers.

I don't know if they would have been better off divorced. I do know that I wouldn't be here to tell their funny stories, like the time she was waiting for the light outside the Lubbock Hotel. Here came Fred, book under arm, against the light, on his way into the hotel, where he would have an expensive lunch and read his book in the lobby. The lobby would be full of old ranchers and cowboys who would stare at Fred in his elegant suit and his hat, wondering who he was. They never knew.

On the street that day he bumped into Kate, knocking her off the curb into the street, where she staggered around, trying to regain her footing. Of course, he didn't see her and walked on. A woman who saw it said to her, "Wasn't that the rudest old man you ever saw in your life?" Kate, breathing hard and trying to stay calm, looked at her for a long while. "My dear woman," she said, "you do not know the HALF OF IT!!!"

MY MOTHER'S CROW

My mother had a crow. Or the crow had her. However it was, she called him Jim Crow, not knowing the implications of the words. She said that she thought it came from Uncle Remus.

The day the crow came, I was sitting in the bay window dreaming about my wedding, which was to be the following year, and contemplating my leaving Lubbock forever. When I saw him, he was staring at our house. "Ma," I called, "come see this weird bird. I think it's a raven." "No," she said, "it's a crow." The crow hopped down the sidewalk, turned in at our front walk, and came right up to the door. He rapped on the door with his beak. Suddenly, there came a tapping, as of someone gently rapping, rapping at our chamber door. I hate myself for it, but I can never resist saying this every time I recall that day.

My mother opened the door and said, "Come right in, Jim Crow!" In he came and stood staring at us with his bright, critical eyes.

We stared back in astonishment. He then inspected the room, fluttering to the tops of the bookcases and tables, pausing and studying intently each little object with which Ma cluttered her living room. He went through the whole house in this manner. We followed, I with trepidation and Ma with absolute glee. When he was satisfied with the place, he went to the kitchen and let loose an ear-splitting cawing and squawking, an unearthly noise for that small room.

Ma hurriedly fixed him a big bowl of cornbread covered with black-eyed peas. He scarfed it up, making what can only be described as guttural noises. When every crumb was gone, he sighed. If a crow can sigh. Then he rapped on the back door, wanting out. Ma didn't want to let him out, but he started his awful squalling and she reluctantly opened the door.

He wandered through the yard, in and out of the flower beds, flying through the trees. When he was satisfied with the yard, he came in, settled himself in a chair and took a nap. My mother was delighted. If a crow could be lord of the manor, he was. She kept his food and water bowls full and he went in and out at will, though he seldom left home. When he did, it was with his friend, the cat. I find it hard to tell this part of the story; it is so crazy.

A cat that we had never seen before would wait on the front porch. Jim Crow would yell to get out and he and the cat would stroll off. Jim hopping, the cat slinking, a ridiculous pair, they always turned right and went down the walk until they were out of sight. After an hour or so they came back, Jim turning in, the cat going on its way up the walk.

We never knew where they went. Why, oh why didn't we follow them? I have come a ways in this world and there are many roads that I have not taken, but the one that nags at me the loudest is the one that the cat and the crow took. Where did they go? Why weren't we more curious? Maybe nothing seemed strange in Lubbock in the forties. Our house was on Thirty-second Street, near the edge of town. Maybe they went out into the fields and had a picnic of grasshoppers. Maybe, maybe, maybe. Fifty years later, I still wonder.

In a poem that my older daughter wrote about my mother she said,

> *In town there was a house*
> *That grew grandchildren and zinnias,*
> *Sweet pecans cracked by the rocker.*
> *A crow lived there, your pet.*
> *He rode your head to burn the trash.*
> *He pecked my mother's toes.*

Jim Crow did ride my mother's head when she took the trash to the alley. The minute that she started gathering it up, he became ecstatic, jumping and whooping around. As she went out, he landed on her head, riding in and out. She was short and fat and her hair was still thick and black. Crowned by the crow, she looked like some sort of peculiar shaman wearing a magnificent black helmet. But he never pecked my toes. Actually, he was rather fond of me. It was my sister Bob that he hated. She didn't care for animals; she barely tolerated dogs and hated cats. I thought it a serious flaw in her character.

Bob was a sun-worshipper, though, and she would go out barefooted and nearly naked. Jim Crow, lurking in the morning glories on the back porch, would attack her toes unmercifully. While she lay out on her quilt, smiling at the sun, he would mutter around, grumbling and croaking at a safe distance.

My mother sometimes had her old friends over, all ladies from Memphis, who then lived in Lubbock. When they were settled with their tea, she let Jim Crow in. He was big and black and out of place. He was also suspicious of visitors and walked in with his wings dragging the floor, squawking and making his most horrible noises. The ladies screamed and spilled their tea. Ma got such a charge from this; she was, really, a perverse woman. Or at least, she had a perverse sense of humor, which she shared with Jim Crow. When he had sufficiently scared the old ladies, he retreated to the kitchen and sat on a chair back making little snorting sounds, his laugh.

Ma had had Jim Crow for nearly five years when she let her little neighbor children take him to school in a cage for a pet show. He was stolen, cage and all. Ma grieved for him, watching the doors for months, thinking that she heard his knock. She claimed that she didn't care for pets. We had many dogs and cats through the years and they were lots of trouble for her. She named all of my cats Fool—White Fool, Gray Fool, etc.—but she was inordinately fond of that bird. We thought that her Indian blood, from a Cherokee grandmother, might have caused her to have such an affinity with him. Some plains tribes considered the crow sacred as the bird of the ghost dance, and others thought him an omen of many things.

I lived a year with Jim Crow before I married, and I was glad to leave him. The Cherokee blood must have thinned out before I got mine. Nothing happened that he didn't consider his business. While I read, he watched my book with his mutters, snuffles, and awks. When I wrote, his beak was at my pen; he was the consummate curious crow. He never just cawed, but had a large repertoire of idiotic sounds. When the sun rose, he made them all if our eyes were still closed.

Years later, my husband, younger daughter, and I were in Mexico, down on the Baja. My daughter and I were looking at the landscape with our awed, artist eyes, when we realized that a crow was hanging around with us. We were in a mystical mood and we were in the right place for it. We were reading Castaneda's book about the old sorcerer who could change himself into a crow. My daughter kept asking our crow, "Is that you, Don Juan?"

After my mother's death, one of her granddaughters, who had raised three children alone and remarried happily, was going back to school to get her long-delayed degree. Ma had so wanted this for her. On her first day at school she was crossing the campus when a crow started following her. When she moved, the crow moved. When she stopped, the crow stopped, all the way across the campus. When she reached the steps of her building, he was in a tree not twenty feet away. She stared at him a long, long while. The crow stared back. Finally, she called out, *"Is that you, Grandma?!"*

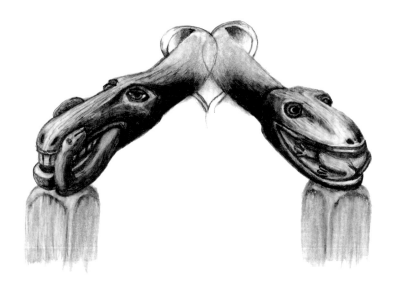

ON BEING PERFECT

When my husband, Paul, and I were young, he always asked me, on coming home from work, "What did you do today?" This was not an idle question. At breakfast, he would have mentioned a couple of things that needed doing. I might or might not have done them, but would come up with something. To spare his feelings, I refrained from mentioning that I had read a lot of old magazines.

Paul was a beautiful man. He had big, round, green eyes, heavy eyebrows, fringy thick eyelashes, a sculpted nose and a wonderful, sensual mouth. Our daughters have his mouth, praise God. He was six feet tall. We met in the summer when we were seventeen. Until the day he died, forty-four years later at 3:30 one morning, I never tired of looking at him.

I was jerking sodas in my family's drugstore down on Avenue H in Lubbock when we met. Our malts were ten cents, but after the ninth malt, the tenth was free. He drank his tenth before he asked me out. He was a cautious man. I wasn't physically attracted to him; he was too skinny. He came to the drugstore in a truck full of flowers. He had worked since he was thirteen for the Texas Floral Company and he called himself "the Texas Kid." I thought he was nineteen because he was a sophomore at Texas Tech and I was only about to be a freshman. He allowed me to believe it, thinking it gave him an advantage, which it did. I was typing some veteran's forms for him after the war and was surprised to learn that we were the same age.

For our first date, Paul brought a little record player to my house and taught me to rumba. In junior high and high school he had worked every day and weekends, never learning to dance. At Tech, he found that he had to dance. So, of course, he was taking lessons. So he could be perfect.

Paul was born to work and he was the worst kind of perfectionist. No, not the worst kind, he was the best kind. The worst kind of perfectionist is one who will be perfect or will not be. Whatever Paul attempted to do, he would be at it until it was perfect or as near perfect as he could make it.

He married the wrong woman.

His worst flaw, if a perfect man can have one, was that he expected everyone to be perfect. He could not face the fact that us ordinary, ornery people will seldom do the right thing, or will do it poorly. At the museum school I had an art teacher, Dorothy Hood, who was a famous and near-perfect painter. She would stop at my easel when I was trying too hard and say, unnecessarily, "Leave a little flaw. Leave a little flaw." The striving for perfection made her nervous. Perfection is impossible. There are flaws in it. Ah, so.

When we were newlyweds living in a tiny garage apartment, I would cook a nice supper. I was not a perfect but a reasonable cook. After supper, Paul would say, "Do you suppose we could paint these walls tonight?" or "Do you suppose we could wax the floors tonight?" *Huh?* I had supposed that we would snuggle up on our new couch. After our honeymoon was over, he quit saying "we" where housework was concerned. I began to suspect that he was not a perfect man.

I got a job so we could buy a car. We were born so poor that neither we nor our families had ever owned a car. We saved every nickel for two years and bought a black 1950 Chevrolet. It looked like an Oldsmobile. We worshipped that car. I would go out early from work so I could see him drive up in it. He was handsome behind its wheel. We had walked or ridden buses for twenty-six years when we bought it.

At the proper time, he took it for the first oil change. He called, saying he would be late. I could barely recognize his voice. He said, *"This fool has put the oil in the radiator!"* The fool, if he lived, is probably traumatized to this day. Paul could not suffer fools.

We lived in Houston, where it was *so hot* before air conditioning. Coming from Lubbock, we found that heat a new kind of suffering. We built a little house after Leslie, our first daughter, was born. Paul, an engineer, was designing the first air conditioning of buildings. He put ducts in our attic for cool air. Our second daughter, Katy, was born. Our house was still hot. By then, the neighbors all had window units. They were cool; we were still sweating like dogs. Finally, Paul was able to buy a discarded unit from some building. We were the only people in the neighborhood with central air conditioning. Paul would never buy anything unless he could pay for it and it was the right thing to buy.

I often think of that little house, beyond the Shamrock Hotel way out off South Main. It was beautiful with its white crushed marble roof and pink Mexican brick. Do the people in it today wonder why they are the only ones in that now poor neighborhood with central air conditioning? Do they wonder about the well with which they water their yard? Paul dug it by hand when our water bill went up during a drought. I drove down that beautiful little street some years ago. I haven't been back. It was dirty and bedraggled; I couldn't bear to look at our house. I was glad Paul couldn't see it.

Before his father died when Paul was five, his father and uncle had been ham radio operators in Lubbock, likely the only ones. Paul built a ham radio and, with the help of a friend, put up a twenty-foot antenna on the roof of our little house. He studied all summer, learning Morse code and getting his license and his call letters. And then he found that the radio guys called him at two or four o'clock in the morning to talk radio. Alas, he wasn't interested. His only fun was talking to an engineer in South America who was working in the jungles on the Pan-American Highway. When he lost contact with the engineer, he took down that antenna and sold it with his handmade radio. He loved the building of the radio, but not the use of it.

He was the same way with guns. He loved guns, but not the use of them. Years later, when he could afford it, he collected them. He loved to take them apart and clean them; he loved the way they looked and their workmanship. But he wasn't keen on firing them. He went goose hunting once a year for business reasons, and only occasionally shot skeet. But he never tired of or sold those guns. I did it for him the year he died. I hate guns. I wish I had melted them down.

When we lived in that first little house, he would say as he left for work, "Do you suppose you could fold all those diapers and my underwear?" When he came home with his what-did-you-do-todays, I would say, "I washed." I loved to devil him.

We were so different.

He was the ultimate engineer, reserved, dignified, quiet.
He dressed in very conservative clothes. On the other hand,
I never shut up and never wore, if I could help it, what were
known in the sixties and early seventies as "grown-up
clothes." I tried constantly to loosen him up, with small suc-
cesses. He finally wore white socks with shorts, and he once
bought a blue-and-white-striped summer suit. I loved him in
it. His car was immaculate; his workshop looked like an oper-
ating room. He painted it white, and his tools (one for everything that needs doing in this world) hung in perfect rows.
A vacuum on his saws and sanders caught even a speck of
sawdust. In the house, his towel was always hung neatly on
its rod, and he never, ever dropped even a sock on the floor.
His closet was the epitome of neatness.

While I was a yellow-dog Democrat, he was a Republican
except for one vote for Kennedy and his years of loving
Lyndon Johnson. I voted for Eisenhower. Otherwise, though
we always voted, we might as well have stayed home. In the
sixties, I went to art school. I painted a series of paintings
with black bands across the bottom to symbolize the black
armbands worn for the moratorium against the Vietnam war.
Later, he saw my name in the paper with artists who had
donated paintings for George McGovern's campaign. He
came home in shock. I had to treat him very tenderly and
bring his supper on a tray. I was Paul's cross to bear and he
had to bear it. He bore it well. He didn't kill me.

In 1961, we moved into a bigger house. We had acquired two
cars. Mine was the car of my dreams and still is—a white Ford
station wagon with red leather upholstery. We had a two-car
garage with a center post. That center post seemed to have a
magnet—I kept scraping it when I backed out. Paul became
irate after about three scrapings and his polite do-you-sup-

poses became rantings-and-ravings. I almost felt obligated to scrape the post. I inherited a perverse nature, and I loved to watch him inspect my car and the post when he came home from work in his dark suit and his striped tie.

One morning, after one of the center post incidents, Paul went out to go to work. I was in the kitchen when I heard the horrible noise. I rushed out, thinking the garage had fallen on him. His car was on the driveway, the garage door draped over its top with wood and glass everywhere. I looked into the car. He looked back. I began to chuckle. I had grasped my ribs and bent over, my mouth open for a laugh that would have been heard on Braes Bayou, when he got out of the car. He gave me a look that would have chilled me to my very bones, if I could have been chilled, and he said, *"Go back in the house!"* I went back in the house. Paul picked the pieces of the door off his car, stacked them neatly to the side and drove off.

When I had finished my laughing, I began to devise my garage-door look. I practiced a startled look, but settled on a wide-eyed, blank-eyed look with a small Mona Lisa smile.

That day, a man came and replaced the door. He removed the wreckage and swept the tail-light glass and the debris off the drive. When Paul drove in that afternoon, his car had been repaired, tail lights replaced, the bashed-in back of his car like new. When he came in, I kissed him like I did every day and gave him my look. It would have cowed him, if he could have been cowed. Until the day he died, I never, ever said so much as one word about that garage door, but he always recognized the garage-door look. If he even felt like storming around the house about one of his many aggravations, I would give him the look. It had a magical effect. A picture is worth a thousand words.

In 1970, we moved into our third house. It was an old New Orleans style house in River Oaks. Paul didn't want it. He hated old, dirty things. I wanted it so badly that I went around mournful until he reluctantly made a ridiculous offer. He had forgotten about it and was shaving one morning when the agent called to tell us that we had it. I waited until he had finished shaving to tell him, for fear he would cut his throat.

Paul worked and spent money on that house until it was clean and new. He gave me money to buy some new things for it. The first thing I bought was a bench for the entryway. I found it in a junk shop down on Montrose Boulevard. It was an old Mexican bench with beautiful flowers carved on its back, but its arms were strange. One arm was a carved monkey with a snake in its mouth; the other a snake with a frog in its mouth. It was perfect. When I came home triumphantly with it, Paul came out to help me bring it in. His eyes glazed over as he sat down on the steps. "You have such strange taste," he said. I had to put that bench up in Katy's room. Katy has the bench today; it is one of her fondest possessions.

Paul spent a lot of money on his daughters' educations, although he hated spending money. He had been so very poor as a child that he had a terrible fear of poverty and wanted his daughters to be engineers, or scientists, or secretaries—anything that they might be self-sufficient. One is a painter. One is a poet. It was the way it was and he had to bear it.

In a poem called "The Dwarf," Wallace Stevens wrote, "The web is woven and you have to wear it. The winter is made and you have to bear it. . . It is all that you are, the final dwarf of you, that is woven and woven and waiting to be worn, neither as mask nor as a garment but as a being." I think of that poem when I consider our marriage and the way we were, fussing, sometimes shouting, but always loving. I wouldn't have given it up for the world.

Paul was not perfect, but his goal was to be perfect. I was his dwarf and he dragged me, kicking and screaming and clutching at the bedpost, with him toward it. He won, after all, our thirty-seven-year battle. Not the battle of the sexes, but the battle of to be or not to be.

Against my will, I inherited some of his traits. I want things that I wasn't born to want. I want my bills paid. I want my house and yard and car clean and well maintained. I want my daughters to be perfect women. I want my granddaughter, Carrie, to be perfect. She is. The only bad thing Paul ever did to me was to make me frugal. I *hate* being frugal. I can't even stand the word. It is an ugly word. Frugal. Oooh! Nevertheless, here I am, nearly old and completely frugal.

Paul Nail made me what I am today, and the only thing that I could ever, *ever* make him do was to eat squash.

EULOGY FOR EGGS

I cooked green eggs and gray bacon on the first day of our honeymoon. I should have had breakfast in New Orleans, but I woke up in Houston in Paul's little garage apartment, which contained a rented bed and chair. It is hard to believe, but there were few apartments in Houston in 1948, except for some garage ones, here and there. Paul had lived in a room, with a roommate, his first year in Houston. But he had a new job when we married, making three hundred and fifty dollars a month, and had rented this apartment in West University Place for seventy-five dollars. I had opted for furniture instead of New Orleans. Bad choice. Little did I know about anything.

Our wedding day was the longest day that I had ever spent in Lubbock. We had raced to the airport to evade Paul's fraternity brothers, who were threatening to take us to Floydada in the back of a pickup. We were met instead at the airport, where "just-married" signs were hung on our backs. The airline served us a special dinner with champagne. Airlines were different then. After dinner, the pilot called our attention to a big, beautiful rainbow, a good omen, he said, and he turned the plane sharply to the right so that he could fly under it. My first flight—it gave me a queasy stomach. And then, unfortunately, more champagne was passed around.

Anyway, I woke up the next morning and was faced with *breakfast*. I washed my face, put on a dab of lipstick and went, the way of all flesh, to the refrigerator, feeling so sexy in my half-priced nightgown. Ah-hah! I found a dozen eggs, a pound of bacon, and some ancient bread. The bacon smelled odd, but I put it on and cut the mold off the bread, getting it ready to toast. The eggs, oh, the eggs! The yolks were an ugly greenish orange and they had a really bad, skunky smell, having been bought when Paul rented the apartment, four months previously. I scrambled them, feeling really green and shaky. I suggested that we not eat the eggs, saying that I wasn't hungry and the eggs were too old to eat. Paul scoffed, saying how lucky he was to have married a woman who could cook, and ate them all. Five. I had cooked two each, and one for the pan. I watched him all morning, wondering where the hospital might be and thinking that if he doesn't die today, he never will.

He did die thirty-seven years later. My cooking did not kill him.

I cooked eggs, though, every morning for almost twenty-five years. I bought at least two dozen per week. We had them over-easy, fried in bacon fat. We had them scrambled in butter, delicate and creamy, with hot, buttered biscuits. M.F.K. Fisher scrambled eight eggs with a half pint or more of rich cream. I never had any cream, but used a big dollop of whole milk and cooked them in butter. Same thing. (Fisher's "recipe for a shrew" called for four eggs, four tablespoons of water, stirred fast in oil.) We had eggs souffléed with cheese and ham. We had them scrambled for supper with grits, the whole covered with chili. I boiled them, deviled the yolks, and piled them, pale and delicious with mayonnaise, pickles, olives and hot sauce, into the whites. A similar concoction, called egg salad, made sandwiches for school, lunch, and picnics. I made Eggs Foo Yung with mushrooms, bean sprouts, green peppers and onions, three eggs per person, covered with a chicken soy sauce. If someone was sick, I made them creamed eggs in a white sauce with butter over toast. When I was a sick child, my mother whipped up a raw one in a glass of whole milk with sugar and vanilla. I did the same for us. I made pies, four-egg cakes, and cookies each week. The pies—custard, chocolate and banana cream with high meringues—were made with eggs, from my *Joy of Cooking*. On Sunday we had pancakes, made with an egg, covered with butter and maple syrup.

And then there was Easter. Two daughters dyed a dozen each, and we went on a boiled egg diet. We had them with asparagus in a rich cream sauce at least twice. And creamed with tuna over toast more than once.

I searched out fresh eggs, and for a long while had an egg man who brought them from his farm. They "stood up," as eggs are supposed to do, in a small round shape in the pan, their yolks high, lovely, and golden.

Paul worked so hard with ten and twelve hour days, that I felt obligated to give him a hot breakfast. What else is hot for breakfast, except oatmeal? We had it only occasionally in the winter.

When we learned that eggs would kill us, we began to eat cereal with fruit. Why, I don't know; Paul had low cholesterol until he died and I still do. I felt ridiculous, setting the table in the early mornings, pouring cold, low-fat milk over a bowl of cold, dry cereal. I was a night person, Paul a morning one. After a while, I gave it up and stayed in bed drinking coffee. Paul learned to get his own cereal.

Roald Dahl said that breakfast cereal is made of all those little curly shavings from pencil sharpeners. I believe him. I eat it, though, most mornings. Not because I fear eggs, but because I am lazy and have no motive to cook a hot breakfast. But I miss those cold, early mornings over our hot plates; Paul dressed, bright-eyed and talking, me slouched over in an old wrapper, barely able to murmur.

Sometimes, on cold, dark mornings, I get my old iron skillet out and cook three slices of bacon until they are brown and crisp. I drop two eggs into that bacon fat over a low fire and, when the whites are barely cooking around the edges, I flick the fat over them until the yellows are glazed over. I butter two pieces of brown toast. I pour a cup of real coffee. I sit down in what seems to be that same old wrapper. "What the hell," I murmur to myself.

And then, I eat that wonderful, warm, yellow stuff and the dark day turns sunny side up.

AN OLD REGRET

I had a friend in Houston way out on Piney Point Road. She lived out there in an old farmhouse when everything past Post Oak Road was still "out there." Lydia was a Czechoslovakian woman with pretty blue eyes and blond hair, but she was sort of a square person, with a square jaw and a square body. She was prettier than she seemed to be. She was my landlady before she became my friend. My young husband and I had rented a tiny house attached to her garage, because we wanted to live in the country. Lydia worked night and day, kept chickens, took in sewing, sold eggs and vegetables and looked after her five acres.

I used her washing machine and in return helped her with her sewing. It was while we were sitting at her kitchen table, putting in hems, that we became friends and she told me the story of her life. She had grown up near a Czech town somewhere in central Texas. (I wish I knew where. I would love to see it.) As a small child, she arrived for her first day of school in a black dress that reached to her ankles, a long black scarf tied over her hair. The children followed her across the schoolyard, laughing and taunting. She was told that they were asking if she were an old woman. She couldn't answer because she spoke no English.

Her parents, who lived with her on Piney Point, had come to Texas as small children. They were in their eighties when I knew them, but they had never spoken a word of English. They had grown up and lived until old age in the Texas countryside near a Czechoslovakian town, reading Czech newspapers, dealing with Czech merchants, and had felt no need for English.

Texas is such a strange place. Lydia told me that the year they came to her house, her father had run through the kitchen one day with his shotgun. She grabbed the gun and had to wrestle him to the floor, shouting, "What is it?!" He said that there was a crazy man outside. The crazy man was a neighbor, clad only in shorts and sandals, coming down the long lane with a basket for his eggs. The father had never seen anyone in shorts. A strange thing, for Texas in the late forties.

I was twenty-six years old and had worn shorts for most of my life. I was wearing them when he taught me to garden, giving me two seventy-five–foot rows in his very large field. He taught me, without English, how to prepare my long rows, making little mounds with fertilizer for my black-eyed peas, okra, tomatoes and cantaloupes. All the while I was wearing shorts, but he always averted his eyes, looking off. It gave us a double problem, the father with no English and no gaze; me with no Czech and no look at his eyes through which to read his mind. Nevertheless, he was a great gardener and he taught me how to do it.

He and his wife were smiling and glad to see me when in a dress, but when I was in my shorts, their eyes were grave, fixed on a distant point. His wife worked in the kitchen, cooking, cleaning, and canning, always in a long, dark dress with a long scarf tied over her hair and under her chin, even in the summer before air conditioning. She was a tiny woman. I never knew or heard her name. She was just Lydia's mother and the old man's wife.

Lydia had a pretty young daughter by a first marriage and was married to Harry. I think that was his name. It was so long ago. Harry was a skinny, slight man with thinning hair and dark, sorrowful eyes. He was always smiling, but his eyes never smiled.

I think he worked for the post office, but he was a cook by trade. Lydia believed it a sin to be idle, so Harry was always working on weekends around the house and mowing the front two acres. But sometimes on a Sunday afternoon they would sit under a big oak, Harry's head on her lap, and she would stroke what hair he had. She was mad about Harry.

While I lived with them they had a baby boy, and I drove her to the doctor when she was too big to drive, and to the baby doctor for the baby's care. I was very fond of Lydia; I had never known anyone like her. She met Harry at the USO. I think he was a cook in the merchant marine.

Lydia said that Harry had once had a great sorrow and he carried in his billfold a picture of a smiling woman, his first wife, with two pretty children. He said that they were killed in a train wreck.

They had a big old dog named Sport. Sport allowed no other dogs on the premises. He was a good dog, but when another dog happened in the front gate, he became a snapping, snarling maniac. He killed a dog and badly injured several others. One day, I was expecting an old friend and had just gotten out of the shower. I was wearing only some transparent, flesh-colored underwear that some nut had given me as a joke for a wedding present. Out the window I saw my friend Dorothy trying to coax her new puppy, a tiny Scotty, out from under the car. And I saw Sport racing toward them, his hackles raised, head down, teeth bared. I ran out, tackled Sport and rolled around on the gravel, hanging on while he lunged toward the puppy, dragging me along. Now Lydia saw this and she thought I was nude. But did she come out to help me? No. She sent Harry. She wasn't a fun-loving woman, but she did love a little excitement.

While we were there with them, Lydia began to sell her land. We bought the back two acres, borrowing $1,800. It scared us to death, owing that much money. She sold the front three acres to the Baptist church for not much more. They moved away to Bryan or College Station and opened a café, where Harry could ply his trade. After that, I never spoke to Lydia again or even wrote to her. It haunts me, because she needed me.

Some time later, Sygmund Byrd, a wonderful columnist who wrote for the old *Houston Press*, wrote a story about Lydia and Harry. Harry had gone down to the café early one morning, put the coffee on, got the café ready for the day, and then he hung his apron on its peg, put on his hat, and disappeared. He was gone.

Sygmund said that Harry had left Lydia's car in Beaumont, the gas tank full, oil newly changed, and the key over the visor. In the story, Lydia said that it proved how much he cared, that he wouldn't want her to pick up the car in bad shape. She thought that he had probably shipped out as a cook on a boat. Lydia put ads in the Houston papers asking Harry to come home. "Come home, Harry," she said. "The taxes are paid and all is forgiven. Your boy misses you. We love you, Harry. Come home."

I don't know if Harry came home—Lord, how I wish I knew— but I think about it once in a while, late at night. I doubt he did. Because he abandoned Lydia, I wondered if his first wife was really killed in a train wreck. I doubt it. I think he just took off when the going got tough. I so regret that I never called Lydia, offering help, or at least sympathy. I knew at the time where she was. I could have gotten her number from information, but I never called. Shakespeare said, "What's gone and what's past help, should be past grief." But Lydia is often on my mind.

She had been there when *I* needed *her*. I had a miscarriage out there, hemorrhaging, and was very ill. She cleaned my house, brought our food, and when I was too weak to stand, she was there to lift me up. And she had an old, tame black and white horse. I was afraid of horses, but she made me ride him every day up and down Piney Point Road and Memorial Drive. She said he needed the exercise, but she really wanted me to get over my fear. We picked dewberries on her back acres, carrying long sticks to punch in the vines for snakes, and she taught me to make dewberry pies.

I never think of her without smelling all of those old pines out on Piney Point, when it was beautiful country—no cars, only the woods, a few houses, and little country lanes. It was *so* green. I see Lydia's great garden, taste all those vegetables, and remember her Czechoslovakian ways.

I wonder if I ever loved Lydia. I should have; I know she loved me. I wonder to this day why I never offered her help when she needed it. I wonder if she is alive. I wonder if Harry came home.

I wish I had a picture of her with her children. I could carry it around and show it to people, saying, "This woman and her children were friends of mine long ago, but they were killed in a train wreck."

CALLING TO THINGS
THAT HAVE VANISHED

Why, oh why, do we have to lose the things we lose? On cold, dark days, I sometimes wander around my quiet widow-house like the motherless child that I am, talking to myself and wondering aloud, "Oh, why?" One of my former sons-in-law, in a song he wrote about choices and opening wrong doors, said that it wasn't ours to choose, "that's why it hurts so bad to lose the stuff we lose." In the song, seven angels stared from a vacant lot, saying, "Our mercy is an open door; it's the other door that's not." I don't need seven angels to tell me that. My sons-in-law are both "former." Oh, I still have them, but I've lost my legal kinship to them and I seldom feed them turkey and dressing. When my generation married, our parents almost always kept their sons- and daughters-in-law forever, for better and for sometimes much worse. In my children's generation, there aren't many forevers.

I want my boys back.

My old sister Bob has lost her memory, or most of it. She is a happy woman, though, and says that it is a blessing, really, as so many things have happened in this world that bear forgetting. And she doesn't have to buy nearly so many books; she reads her favorites over and over and they are always new. I want her memory back. I want her to remember with me our good times. Unfortunately, she has some memories of the distant past that would be better lost. She remembers being at the station late in the afternoon when they brought Freddy home.

Freddy was our big brother, a beautiful boy with black eyes and hair. He was funny and always up to something. When he was nine, he led his Sunday school class out on strike. His teacher, very agitated, confronted my mother after church with the bad news. At dinner, which we always had at noon, my mother said, "Freddy, I hear that your class went out on strike. Why?" He said that it wasn't a real strike, that he just suddenly thought that Broom's Creek was a better place to be. Freddy and his class had gone down to the creek, taken off their Sunday shoes and played in the water until church was out. Ma didn't scold him; in fact, she thought it an innovative thing to do on a summer Sunday morning. She chuckled around all afternoon.

He was already working downtown when I was old enough to remember. My brother John and I would watch and wait for him to come home. He came with his hands behind his back full of gum or candy and we would play the old, old game. Oh, how we loved him. I want him back.

He was mad about baseball and was playing when a ball hit him in the back of his head. He was knocked out, but he got up and finished the game. The ball bruised his brain and he developed meningitis from the blow. My father and uncle took him on the train to Dallas, a hopeless trip before antibiotics. Why couldn't that ball have waited just a few years? They said that when he died at five o'clock in the morning, he was shouting, "Play ball! Play ball! Play ball!" My mother said that she heard the mourning doves at five and knew that he was gone.

I was only four, but Ma held me up and I patted his face as he lay in his coffin at church. A friend said, "Don't let her do that!" My mother said, "Why not?" Even at four, I knew he was not just asleep and I knew from all the tears that he was lost to us.

Afterward, my mother would call him her "Little Boy Blue" from Fields' poem of the same name. "The little toy dog is covered with dust, the little toy soldier is red with rust" and "In the night, an angel came and awakened our Little Boy Blue." I'm not sure if those lines are right; I have lost the poem, but she would repeat all of those sad old lines and weep and weep. I can hear her yet.

Freddy was fourteen when he died; he would be eighty now, a grand old man. He was my first sorrow, and I still have it.

When I was in the second grade, I had pneumonia. There were still no antibiotics, and I almost became the "lost" instead of the "loser." During my recovery, I read constantly from our little books, *The World's 101 Best Poems.* We called them "the little blue books." They were full of hokey poems—"Let me live in a house by the side of the road" and "Only God can make a tree"—but I learned to love poetry from them. We lost them during one of our many moves. They were given away or thrown out. I know who did it, but she is in her grave and I can't reach her . . . yet. I would give a million for those little blue books.

My sister, the one who's lost her memory, called herself Roberta Victoria, though her name is Bobby Ayers. She also bossed John and me around because we were the babies. She made us memorize poems from the blue books and would have a recital. She arranged the dining chairs in the living room facing the French doors to the dining room, where John and I recited. She charged two cents for admission and always had a full house. Long, long before I ever attended poetry readings, we didn't know that you could read from a book. We had to know the poems "by heart." I love the term. John and I were both good, but I was perfect.

I always said a poem narrated by the father of a little Italian boy who, during a cold, cold winter, was dying in a New York tenement. He had "a leetle pot of what you call forget-me-nots" and they were also dying. The little boy kept hoping for spring, so that he could put them on the window sill to save them. I was just right for the poem, still leaning to the left from a collapsed lung, bone thin, hair mostly gone from fever—the perfect picture of a dying child. Tears ran down faces when I, in the most dramatic manner that I could manage in my weakened condition, said the last lines: "The spring is come, but oh, da joy, eet was too late. My leetle boy, he no could wait."

I know how that boy wanted his "leetle pot" of forget-me-nots to live. It makes me lonesome just thinking about it. I always think of that old poem when I read Roethke's "Geranium." I did a sad painting once called "My Geranium is Dying" from his poem, but I was thinking of the forget-me-nots. Roethke's geranium died, though he tried to save it, and even after it died, he loved it and kept it for company. He came home one day and found that his maid had thrown it out. "I sacked the presumptuous hag," he said. "I was that lonely."

I want my little blue books.

SWING LOW, SWEET CHARIOT

It is the durnedest thing to get old. I'm not old yet. I'm only seventy, but my knees are creaky and I sometimes seem to be tottering toward the bathroom in the mornings. In fact, my once-beautiful legs don't look like my legs at all. Something odd is going on with my upper arms and I can't find my waist. And I have strange dreams of people long gone. I often dream that my husband, who left this world innocent at sixty-one, ran off with another woman. In the dream, I see her everywhere with him and he has no shame. I wake up as mad as the devil on these mornings and do some manual labor. When he was still here, he never even dreamed of looking at another woman, but when he made me mad, I would clean the house like a demon. I am seldom angry now. My house is in bad shape.

So far, though, growing old is not bad, just peculiar. It would help if body and mind could agree. My body knows very well that it's seventy, but my mind won't touch it with a ten-foot pole. This intellectual refusal to grow old evidently runs in the family. My mother complained about it in her eighties. She had two friends who were senile and she said that she envied them. "There they are," she said, "smiling all day, someone taking care of them, and they don't give a hoot." She thought she would be happier if her mind could wander a bit. "It's a God-awful thing," she said, "to have a twenty-five-year-old mind in an eighty-five-year-old body."

She and my dad retired to Lorenzo, where my sisters lived, near Lubbock, seven miles past Ida Lou. She was riding into Lubbock one day (she didn't drive, had never had a car) with her friend Babe. Babe was younger, only eighty. They had gone to town to buy chickens on sale. On the way home, Babe swerved off the road into the rear of a big truck parked by the highway. They were stunned and bruised, their laps full of dead chickens, but Babe backed up and went home. Her husband, seeing the bashed-in front of the car, rushed off to the scene of the accident, warning Babe not to even touch her car until he returned. Babe, knowing that Ma had bought catfish and was planning to fry them, got on her big tricycle and rode six blocks to Ma's house. Her tricycle, a strange affair, was a cross between bicycle and tricycle, with two big back wheels. They were popular in the seventies for the elderly. I haven't seen one since.

Ma's right leg, at the time of the accident, was full of arthritis. Her foot had turned inward and she was walking around on its side. It was morning, after the wreck and the fish fry, before she had time to look at her bruises. Lo and behold, she found her leg straight and her foot flat on the floor. She thought that ramming her leg into the floorboard in the accident had done it. I thought the fright of it had given her a huge jolt of cortisone. Whatever, it was a miracle. Her old leg was well for the short remainder of her life. She was very pleased, considering that she never went to the doctor in her long life without being dragged there. She never took medicine, unless my vigilant sister Loisie was there to see that she swallowed it. Otherwise, she flushed all medicine down the commode, one dose at a time.

She was trying to push a spade into her flower bed when she was about eighty-eight. She had done this every spring for seventy years, preparing her beds for her tomatoes and petunias and zinnias and all of the flowers that she so loved. That day, she couldn't get the spade into the ground. "What in the devil is the matter with my leg?!" she said, examining her old spindly shank. "Oh, damn!" she said, "I forgot. I'm old!"

A year later, after walking her usual twelve blocks to Loisie's house, she fell on the curb and went in bleeding to announce, "I'm too old to live by myself." She moved in with my sister, and the next year she was wrestling a skate-shoe out of some bushes, its laces all entwined, when her aged hip broke and tossed her to the ground. She was ninety.

She recovered from the hip, but a kidney infection from the bed-stay gave her Guillain-Barré Syndrome, a paralysis. A young doctor told us that she could recover. She couldn't have, but we wanted to believe him and allowed them to put her on a ventilator, with the tube and all in her throat. We so wanted her to live. She mouthed words to me in intensive care, and she had cussed me out enough in my life that I could read her lips. She said, "Get me the hell out of here!"

My daddy never noticed that he was growing old. He had a wonderful knack of ignoring unpleasantries. He read, worked, smoked cigars, and drank whiskey, until he curled up into a little ball and died at ninety. He had worked as a hospital pharmacist until he was past seventy-five. They let him go because of his age, but he wouldn't quit. For several years he commuted by bus, living all week in old hotels and working in little drugstores in the country around Lubbock. He finally gave it up at eighty-two. In his late eighties, the arteries hardened in his brain. He was normal during the day, but at night his bloodstream slowed and he had hallucinations. The worst one was a group of Baptists who would file into his room every night, singing hymns and trying to convert him. He was a staunch Methodist. He would come to breakfast, saying, "Oh, I am exhausted. Those Baptists were at it again last night. They will stop at nothing! Will they never give up?!"

Dad had been gone for some years when Ma began to hear voices. She heard them in her hall in the mornings. She was horrified. We had made such a flap when Dad heard voices that she decided to say nothing. They were benign voices, speaking of mundane things. "Did you set out thet trash? You want some biskits with them aigs?" Loisie was there early one morning to take Ma to some to-do and was waiting for her to get ready. She heard the voices. "Who are you talking to?" she asked. Ma said, "Nobody, I'm not talking to anybody." Sister said, "But I hear voices!" Ma said, "THANK GOD!"

We never understood those voices. Ma had an air conditioner over her hall, an old dry-stack type, wet straw and a fan that blew cold air into houses in high, dry country. We decided that it must have been acting like an antenna, somehow picking up the voices of her neighbors, delivering them to the hall. Others have blamed the Baptists.

My old sister, the editor, the one who has lost her memory, had a fine country newspaper, *The Lorenzo Leader*. She is a writer, never published except in her own paper, but never-theless, a writer. She didn't go to college, while I, who would have had a degree in journalism except for French 232, never went near a newspaper. She was in an old cemetery one day, searching for the grave of someone she wanted to write a story about for her paper. She wandered among the ancient stones, reading names and dates, imagining lives, until she got into sort of a transfixed state. She had been there all afternoon and was sitting on a stone at dusk, with the birds twittering around in their sleep and dark coming down, when she heard from a distant highway an air horn from a big truck. She said, "I hear you, Gabriel."

I live in Lakeway now. When my husband and I came here at the end of the seventies, it was a retirement community. Most of us were old or getting there. Today, we are about half old and half young, a great improvement. But there are still many of us (and more always arriving) in the golden age. The golden age—the age of strokes, heart attacks, broken hips and other calamities, when we tend to listen for helicopters. They come, the Starflights, swinging low with their beating wings and ominous sound until they land somewhere. We go out, night or day, to see who it is that they have carried away. And we say, "Well, today, it wasn't me."

Right this minute I am watching some buzzards; ten or so are flying high in the sky. How is it that a bird so horribly ugly can look so wonderful in his flight? But there they are, soar-ing in their graceful, grand, majestic way, floating like a flock of black angels over the beautiful, blue Lake Travis.